THE SENSE OF THE PAST

By

HENRY JAMES

Double9 BOOKS

The Sense Of The Past

by **Henry James**

ISBN: 978-93-57271-84-4

Published by

DOUBLE 9 BOOKS

2/13-B, Ansari Road
Daryaganj, New Delhi – 110002
info@double9books.com
www.double9books.com
Tel. 011-40042856

Printed in India.

ABOUT THE AUTHOR

Henry James, an American-British author, was born on April 15, 1843, and died on February 28, 1916. He is well-known as a key transitional personality between literary realism and modernism. His novels dealt with the social and marital interplay between Americans, English people, and continental Europeans. Author Henry James was nominated for the Nobel Prize for English Literature. His novel, "The Turn of the Screw," is regarded as one of the most analyzed and ambiguous ghost stories in the English language. The Wings of the Dove (1902), The Ambassadors (1903), and The Golden Bowl (1904) were James's three most significant novels. Henry James was the author of 20 novels, 112 tales, 12 plays, several volumes of travel and criticism, and a great deal of literary journalism. A master of prose fiction from the beginning, he practiced it as a fertile innovator, enlarged the form, and placed upon it his own stamp. The Ambassadors is the first in a series of three novels by Henry James, published between 1901 and 1914, dealing with the subject of an heiress doomed to die by illness. This novel avoids its cliché subject by focusing on the characters surrounding the unfortunate young woman.

CONTENTS

PREFACE

THE SENSE OF THE PAST, *the second of the two novels which Henry James left unfinished, had been planned and begun some years before he died. The two first books and a part of the third had been written, and it appears that the idea had been abandoned for accidental reasons, not because he was himself dissatisfied with it. He went back to it again during the first winter of the war, having found that in the conditions he could not then go on with* The Ivory Tower *and hoping that he might be able to work upon a story of remote and phantasmal life. He re-dictated, with slight modifications, the chapters already written, and continued the book at intervals until the autumn of 1915. He was then engaged for a time on other work—the introduction to the* Letters from America of Rupert Brooke. *He had just finished this and was preparing to return immediately to* The Sense of the Past *when on December 2 he was attacked by his last illness. The later chapters of the novel, as they stand, had not been finally revised by him; but it was never his habit to make more than verbal changes at that stage.*

The notes on the course which the book was to follow were dictated when he reached the point where the original draft broke off. These notes are given in full; their part in Henry James's method of work is indicated in the preface to The Ivory Tower.

PERCY LUBBOCK.

BOOK FIRST

They occurred very much at the same hour and together, the two main things that—exclusive of the death of his mother, recent and deeply felt by him—had yet befallen Ralph Pendrel, who, at thirty, had known fewer turns of fortune than many men of his age. But as these matters were quite distinct I take them for clearness in their order. He had up to this time perforce encountered life mainly in the form of loss and of sacrifice—inevitabilities these, however, such as scarce represented a chequered career. He had been left without his father in childhood; he had then seen two sisters die; he had in his twentieth year parted by the same law with his elder and only brother; and he had finally known the rupture of the strongest tie of all, an affection for which, as a living claim, he had had to give up much else. Among these latter things, none the less, he had not as yet had to reckon Mrs. Stent Coyne, and this even though the thought of such a peril was on the eve of his crisis fairly present to him. The peril hung before him in fact, though the first note of the crisis had by that time already sounded, from a different quarter, in the guise of a positive stroke of luck. It appeared that what destiny might call on him for this time would not be just another relinquishment. A letter from a friend in England, a fellow-country-man spending a few months in London and having friends of his own there—had mentioned to him the rumoured grave illness and imminent extinction, at a great age, of the last person in that country bearing Ralph's family name, a person of a distant cousinship with whom he had been indifferently aware. His indifference was not a little enlivened by a remark of his correspondent. "Surely when he does die you'll come in for something!"

"Surely" was a good deal to say and the whole hint fantastic—it took so much for granted; yet the words had an effect. This effect was that Ralph determined to mention the matter on the same occasion as something else the revolving months had charged him with, something he had at last really straightened himself to say to the woman he loved. He had had his fears, and in addition to other hindrances, infelicities of circumstance, imperfections of opportunity, had long deterred him, and he was now disposed to throw himself upon anything that could figure as a help. It might support him to be able to tell her there was a chance for him of a property—probably of some wonderful old house—in England: though less, properly speaking, as an improvement to his state of fortune, which might sufficiently pass, than as a bribe to her sense of the romantic. That faculty had originally been strong in her and what could be more depended on at any time in New York, in Park Avenue, to show as inordinate, as fetching, by the vulgar term, than so possibly to "come in" for something strange and storied, ancient and alien? Aurora Coyne was magnificent; that was where his interest in her and her effect upon him were strongest. Beautiful, different, proud, she had a congruity with things that were not as the things surrounding her, and these usual objects, in whatever abundance, were not the bribe to offer. He was glad, at this hour, that his name, by common consent—above all, always, it was true, in Park Avenue—cast a fine sharp traceable shadow, or in other words that his race had something of a backward, as well as of a not too sprawling lateral reach. He knew how little his possession of more mere money would help him, and also that it would have been in his interest to be personally quite of another type; but that his cleverness could on occasion please her he struck himself as in a position to remember, and he at present, turning the whole case over, found aid in the faith that she might at the worst marry him for curiosity. He was for that matter himself just now inflamed with a curiosity that might prove communicable.

The element of uncertainty at all events, such as it was, came largely from the late changes in her own condition; so far as it was not likewise distinguishably riper fruit of the impression in him, rather heavy from the first, of something that he could only call to himself her greater knowledge of life. He had already more than once had to take into account that of the two she had seen, as people said, much the most of the world; and she had not at present seen less of it for returning to America, after her husband's death in the south of Europe and on the admonition of still other circumstances that he divined as beyond his measure, with something of the large air of a public policy. Her departures, absences, returns, returns as for the purpose of intensifying fresh disappearances, these things were what had somehow caused her to glare at him, to dazzle and almost to blind him, as by a wider initiation. He had seen her thus only at certain points of her sustained revolution; had been ignorant of many things with which the cup of her own knowledge overflowed; had been in short indebted for the extent of his privilege to the mere drops and lapses in the general time, as he termed it, that she so insolently kept. Sharing continuously as a child, and then as a growing girl, the life led by her parents in other countries, she had had behind her, at their first meeting, on their twentieth birthday—for in respect of age they marched well enough together—if not fifty years of Europe at least something that already caused him to view his untravelled state as a cycle of Cathay. The time immediately following had been her longest period at home, as well as that of his happiest opportunity—an opportunity not so enjoyed, however, as to have forestalled her marriage with so different a person and so selected a suitor as Townsend Coyne, which event had in its turn been rich in consequences.

Some of these, like the immediate migration to Europe of the happy couple, as the pair were prefigured, had been of the sort essentially indicated; such others as Coyne's early failure of health during a journey to the East had been unexpected and lamentable. He had reappeared with his wife, after a year or two, in America, where the air of home so reinforced him at first as to make the presumption of their settling for some stay natural; and then, disappointed and threatened afresh, had a second time taken flight with her to spend another term, wearily enough, in consultations and climates. The issue at last, indeed too promptly, had been Coyne's death, foreseen for some months, at Pisa, a place he liked and had been removed to from Florence, choosing it, as he said, in view of the end. Stricken and childless, his young widow had once more crossed the sea and, announcing her purpose of an indefinite rest, had spent in New York another winter, in the course of which Ralph Pendrel, held fast there by his close care of his mother, at this time more of a charge than ever and steadily failing, had repeatedly seen her; all of which, none the less, had not prevented, on Mrs. Coyne's part, the perversity of yet another departure, a step sudden and inconsequent, surprising and even disconcerting to our young man, possessed as he definitely was by that time of the length he would have gone had he been able a little longer to avert it. He had felt a delicacy about proposing marriage to a woman supposedly in grief, certainly in the deepest mourning, so that in again spreading her wings she struck him as having profited a little unfairly by his scruple. It was in fact as if she had gone because knowing what would happen if she didn't; but it was also precisely because she had described herself as now nevermore going that he had, in his delay, taken counsel of the decency with which he supposed she would credit him. Some such credit she had in fact doubtless given to him, but what was the use in New York of an advantage that could be enjoyed—really to call enjoyed—but, for example, in Rome? There were moments in which indeed for that matter he scarce quite knew what he had done for himself—measuring it as so distinct a quantity to have introduced confusion into his friend's sequences. Perhaps after all she had retreated only to mark the more sharply the act of waiting. Wasn't it at any rate something for him to have caused her to give up a plan? The appearance was composed of two elements and might become clearer could these elements somehow be reconciled. He and her plan were not, after all, quantities that should absolutely refuse to mingle, and on the question of the particular something that might be given up for something else the combinations—between two persons not wholly unintelligent—were practically infinite. There might always be something to be gained so long as anything to be renounced was left. And finally in fact when poor Mrs. Pendrel did pass away it was quite as if Aurora had acted in obedience to some such view. She disembarked yet again from the frequent Cunarder, and this time, as appeared and as I have hinted, with a mind fully made up. She at once took possession of the ample house her husband had left her.

She had never been more splendid, it may at once be said, than in the light of the reception she gave him on the morrow of these events: she fed with so free a hand his fancy—all uninstructed as he ruefully confessed it—of her resemblance to some great portrait of the Renaissance. That was the analogy he had, at favouring times, in the approaches to Park Avenue, or perhaps still more in the retreats from it, fondly and consistently found for her: she was an Italian princess of the *cinque-cento*, and Titian or the grand Veronese might, as the phrase was, have signed her image. She had a wondrous old-time bloom and an air of noble security. The roots of her flowering were watered by Wall Street, where old Mr. Coyne and her maternal grandsire, both still in the field and almost equally proud of her, conspired to direct the golden stream; though the plant itself seemed to spring from a soil in which upheavals—when upheavals occurred—offered to panic at least a deeper ground than a fall in stocks. Large calm beauty, low square dresses, crude and multiplied jewels, the habit of watching strife from a height and yet of looking at danger with a practised bravery, were some of the impressions that consorted with her presence. When therefore she had, with whatever kindness, shaken her slow head at Ralph three times, there came to him a sad sense of his having staked his cast, after all, but on the sensibility of a painted picture. She had touched him at other times with a high hardness, whereas at present, clearly, she would have given anything to seem mild; only it was at the end of ten minutes of such mildness as if he stood under her closed window in darkness and sleet.

This brought the truth home to him as it had not yet come: he had nothing in common with her apprehension—so particular, so private as that would be—of the kind of personal force, of action on her nerves and her senses, that might win from her a second surrender. Strange he had always thought it that her first had been, against all the likelihoods, Townsend Coyne, so queer though so clever, so damaged, to the extent even of considerably looking it, yet somehow so little touching in proportion, and so suggestive of experience, or at least of overstrained and ambiguous knowledges, by the large expense of it all, as who should say, rather than by equivalents accruing in the way of wisdom or grace. Ralph reflected as to this, at the same time, that in the case of a relation of that intimacy, really of that obscurity, nothing was appreciable from outside; this was the commonest wisdom of life—little indeed as it governed the general pretence of observation that no one but the given man and the given woman could possibly know the truth, or indeed any of the conditions, of the state of their being so closely bound. It didn't matter now therefore that the conditions of the Coynes had put him a question impossible to answer; the answer was Aurora's own, for whatever future application, whatever determination of her further conduct: she had been admirable and inscrutable—that was the only clearness; though indeed with it one might at a stretch inwardly remark that if the future *did* owe her amends she probably saw them as numerous.

Could she have shown him, at any rate, in a burst of confidence, this compensating vision, he would have liked exceedingly to see it, even at whatever cost to his own pride; but she nursed it now, at least to begin with, in silence, only signing faintly, to his embarrassment, with her grand thick-braided head. What this most suggested to him was that if at twenty-two she had married a condemned consumptive she wouldn't now, at thirty, marry a mere thinker—which was what Ralph amusedly knew himself to pass for in New York, where the character indeed is held almost as much in honour as that of the dervish in the East and where once, at his door, it had been all but set down to him as professional by the man calling about the Census or the Directory. Aurora Coyne's backers, her ancestor and her late husband's, as Park Avenue so often termed grandparents and parents, were members of the local Chamber of Commerce, but he himself should more fitly have been a Malatesta or a Sforza: then she might have been contracted to a despot or a condottiere. Within the quarter of an hour he had completely lowered his crest. "I see, I see," he said, "I'm even less possible to you than I feared; and heaven knows I hadn't sinned by presumption." She continued to say little in reply—so little that, to ease positively for herself the awkwardness of so few attenuations, he risked expressing her view, risked even, for charity, making her contradict him. He imputed to her not quite a wish to dismiss him wounded, yet making her care enough to contradict him would a little diminish his defeat. "The one kind of man you could really fancy would be some big adventurer. You'll marry the day you meet one of your own proportions and general grand style, a filibuster or a buccaneer. You might do with a great soldier—all the more that there are some such about; yet even that is not the exact note. You won't of course confess to it, but he should have a shade of the ruffian. It's a pity there are no more pirates—you'd have doted on Paul Jones. The adventurer isn't enough—your ideal's the desperado. I too, however, in my way, am desperate. But I'm too intellectual."

"You know," she presently replied, "how clever I've always thought you."

"Well then you see how clever I am. I've put my finger straight on the place. You can't deny it. I see you as you are, and you don't see me; so that after all I've in a manner the advantage."

She spoke always but after little intervals; yet not as if to show she had taken one's words in, for his at least were never directly met. "I haven't waited till now to feel that you'd never be happy with me. I'm quite too stupid."

"That's but a way of saying that I'm quite too small. What need have I, all the same, of anyone else's wit?"

"I like men of action," she at last returned. "Men who've been through something."

"And I've been through nothing—I see—but the long discipline of my choked passion for you."

She kept answering—her bold grave eyes fixed on him, counting with nothing, evading nothing—as if she had not heard him. "If it could be a man of your kind at all it would be you. There are things in you I like so. But that you should give up anything for me—that I should find quite horrible. You must become great. Intellectually," she explained as if she quoted it out of a book.

"Yes," Ralph laughed even while he sighed—"dry up to it, shrivel down to it! You *must* despise me to say such a thing as that to me! Why not tell me at once that you hope you may never see me again?"

"You're beautiful," she remarked without pity.

"A beautiful worm?" he asked; "a delicate classified insect? a slow-crawling library beetle, slightly iridescent, warranted compressible—that is resisting the squash—when the book is closed to on him?"

"You're beautiful," she simply repeated.

He appeared at this to take something of it in, or at any rate to make something of it out. "Why won't it just do then that one is a gentleman—and for all that not a fool?"

"Oh it does do—for being glad I know you and that you're just as you are. It's good to know there are people like you—though I assure you I don't dream there are many. You're beautiful," she observed once more.

"Thank you very much!" he observed with frank irritation. "I had rather you found me ugly enough to think of. If I could make out what it is you want one to have done I promise you it wouldn't leave me gaping. What is it, what is it?" he pressed. "There's something you've a fancy for that we're not in the way of—any of us: devilish poor lot as we are! I've at least this superiority, you see, that I want to know it. Name it—come, name it; and no matter how dreadful or how criminal it may be I won't flinch from it."

Still with her eyes on him, and even, as it might have seemed, with the oddest perversity of admiration, she waited after her wont. But when she spoke it was terrible. "Just pursue your studies."

It positively affected him for an instant as a blow across the face, putting a quick flush there and a tear in each eye. "How you must really hate me!" And then as she herself changed colour: "And all because I've written a book!"

Though she changed colour indeed she granted nothing: "Which I've read," she only replied, "with the greatest interest—even if I don't pretend to have understood it all. I hope you'll write many more."

"'Many more'!"—he laughed out. "Charming," he scoffed without seeing where he went, "charming the way you appear to imagine one throws such things off! The idea people have of 'books'——!" He had gone too far before he saw it—had gone so far that the next instant, at the sight of something in her face, there was nothing but to pull up. She really cared, and he had been calling her 'people,' had been grotesquely tilting before her at a shapeless object stuck up by himself, and stuck up crooked. She really cared, yes; yet what was it withal she cared for? He took a different tone in a moment to ask her, and in another she had begun in her own way to tell him.

"I've had in my mind—in connection with my ever marrying again—a condition; but it's a matter I meant to speak of only when driven to the wall, as I'm bound to say I think you've driven me." With which she went on as if it explained everything. "I've come home, you know, to stay."

For Ralph it explained too little; yet as there was something in her look that amplified it he saw more or less what was coming and he smiled without pleasure. "You said that—don't you remember?—the last time."

"Yes, I said it the last time, and you've every right to laugh at it and to doubt it. No one but myself can know that I'm serious, or why, and I can't give my reasons and I dare say I must accept being ridiculous. At any rate," she added with a kind of beautiful grimness, "I shan't parade my ridicule about the world. I shall have it out *here*." The force of her emphasis affected him indeed as strange, but she pursued before he had time to take it up. "I shall never—oh but *never*—go back."

It struck of a sudden a fuller light, and he seemed to understand. There was something she wouldn't, she couldn't name, but her accent alone sufficiently betrayed it. She had had "somewhere abroad," as poor Ralph used so often to put it, an encounter, an adventure, an agitation, that, filling her with rage or shame, leaving behind it a wound or a horror, had ended by prescribing to her, as a balm or vengeance, the abjuration of the general world that had made it possible. What such an accident could have been—to such a woman—was ground for wonder; but Ralph felt easily enough that it was yet none of his affair and that he should even perhaps at no price ever learn it. It had poisoned for her a continent, a hemisphere, and such a hush for the moment fell upon him that he might verily have been in presence of it. While they kept in communication during these instants he at any rate put things together. "The condition you speak of is then that one shall never ask you again to leave this country?"

She shook her head as for pity of his poor vision, though he pretended so to vision. "No. It's worse than that."

Then it was really that he guessed, though there was something in him that couldn't make him eagerly jump to it. "Of course," he vaguely observed, "your having had your fill——!"

"Yes," she sighed with all the meaning his drop didn't grasp, "I've had my fill!"—and she turned away as if he might already now see too much. The next minute, however, she was upon him again with what had to serve for the time as the rest of the story. "It's too monstrous a thing to ask, and I don't ask it. It makes everything so impossible that I should have liked a thousand times better your not speaking to me. It can do, you see, neither of us any good;

for it only offers me as rather crazy—as heartlessly perverse if you like—and yet gives you no hope of curing or redeeming me. I should have to ask, you know," she now fully explained, "for a vow."

He smiled from further off. "That I shall take my oath——?"

"Never yourself to go."

"Not anywhere, you mean?"

Her pause had this time more visible thought. "Nowhere you most want. Oh," she declared, "I know what you most want and what you've a thousand reasons for wanting. I know just what your admirable life has been and how, by so rare a chance, you've been held fast here and prevented. I know you're at last free, and that—except, if you insist on it, your idea about *me*—you've naturally now no other thought in your head but to make up for lost time and repair your sacrifice. That's naturally your necessity much more than the fancied necessity in obedience to which you've spoken to me; and my conviction of this is what makes me bold to speak to you as I do. I don't fear, you see"—she gathered confidence, she gathered even a force of expression she had never known, as she went—"that I shall have it on my conscience that I've succeeded with you. I shall on the contrary simply have exposed myself; which I shan't at all regret, however, if I've helped you to clear up your feelings." To this service of charity in fact, and nothing more, she had finally the air of lending herself, while Pendrel began to take it all from her as if he too saw the truth. It was at the same time characteristic of her that at the moment of indicating the sacrifice she made, the exposure, as she called it, that she consented to, for his ultimate peace, she drove well home the knife she had planted. "My excuse would have been—if there *were* any chance for me—that you happened to be so perfect a case for what I call to myself salvation. One doesn›t easily find a man of your general condition who has not, as we say, 'been'; and much less therefore a man of your particular one. By your particular one," Aurora Coyne wonderfully proceeded, "I mean that of knowing so much that might seem to have been to be got at only by immense experience. You know everything, and yet you've learnt it all over here; some miracle or other has worked for you or—it comes to the same thing!—for my vision of you: I don't know, even with your happy conditions, after all, what it can have been, but it makes you, doesn't it? the single case of your kind. If you had been spoiled there would have been no use—and of course as it is there's none. Only I can't help having just put it to you thus," she wound up, "that you've not been spoiled."

There was no doubt of the nature of the effort made by Pendrel to do these remarks justice. “You do put it to me with the magnificence that attends every breath of your being. I haven’t been spoiled—I see quite what you mean—I only *can* be.»

“You only *will* be,» she said almost tenderly. “You’ll be beautifully spoiled.”

“For *you*, that is, of course,” Ralph went on.

“For me—certainly. Isn’t it only of myself after all that we’re talking?”

He answered nothing and the silence between them was for a little as if she had suddenly given him a chance. This effect moreover grew from what he finally said; which was after he had restlessly moved to the window, looked out thence for some instants and then come back. “You would definitely accept me if I did formally give up everything but this?”—and he jerked his head at the outer world of which he had with such intensity just renewed his impression.

“Ah,” she disappointingly answered, “I don’t absolutely say that.”

Poor Pendrel again stared. “Then what do you say at all? Do you expect me to renounce for nothing?”

“I don’t expect you, as I’ve perfectly told you, in any degree to renounce. Why should you?” she added. “No one will ever have an idea of what you have lost.”

“No one but myself,” he said with his eyes on her.

“Oh I think you will least of all.”

She had answered so straight that it had almost the sound of levity; by the hint of which he was justly enough irritated. “It’s too portentous—what you ask!”

But she found for this her quickest reply. “I don’t ask anything. It’s you who ask. I only answer. I decline the honour of your hand, and I give my reasons. If I had given none I should have been doubtless less absurd, and my reward is that I’m not really sure I should have been even less cruel. I’m sure,” she continued, “but of one thing—or rather perhaps of two: that I’m as insane as you please, but that I’m also as rigid. Don’t think, at all events, that you need, or that you possibly *can*, tell me how my attitude strikes you. Do me the simple justice to believe that I know.”

So she appeared quietly to conclude, and it was in her quietness indeed that her perversity most showed; though this was in a manner an aid, if a lame one, to her suitor, called upon at a moment's notice both to measure its extent and to give up the hope of getting round it. "You call me a 'case,' but it seems to me you're at least as extraordinary a one."

"I didn't apply the term to you abusively," she made sufficient haste to explain. And then as, however she applied it, he but sat, in his hard dilemma, with his head in his hands: "Am I not the first to admit that I can only appear unaccountably exalted—it's the word you must have in your mind about me; and exalted on the subject on which it most seems to people grotesque to be so?" She gave herself up, in fine, as extravagant, maniacal, and then, further, to the moral of it, which was that they lacked all ground for possibly meeting. They must accept their preposterous difference, and she could herself do so the better that she was sure of what he had intended to say to her. He had his plans made; he "sailed," didn't he? next week, next month, next year even, if that should be more convenient to her, and had come to propose that she should sail with him. This was, as he saw, not so much as discussable; but he must go on sailing as if nothing whatever had happened. He must stay a long time, and it was indeed all but a certainty for her that when once he should get well into it he would find himself staying indefinitely. Yes, that was inevitably what must happen to him: he offered the bright example of a man of thirty, with means, curiosity, the highest culture, who had, for whatever reasons, never gone at all, but he would show how people with that history infallibly made it up by never coming back when once they did go. Why *should* he come back? With his tastes, his resources and opportunities, his intensified longing and disciplined youth, he would have an admirable life.

Many things were before him while she talked, but most of all perhaps the almost sinister strangeness of his having been condemned to this ordeal. It was the last predicament he had ever dreamed of, the prescription of further patience least on the cards for him, he would have supposed, and least congruous with other realities. This in fact made her spring of action, the unconfessed influence that had worked in her, constantly less and less doubtful. The difficulty was that though he had everything on his side he actually felt himself in a cleft stick. "Don't you then," he appealed, "just simply and personally care for me the least little bit? What you seem to me to have in your head," he went on after waiting a while in vain for her reply, "is, however you express it, a mere cold little theory, which is rather proud of itself, but which has the peculiarity of being both sophisticated and stupid. I don't quite see, you know, why I should be offered up on such an altar." After which, as she was still silent, though only as if because she had already said all: "Is it inconceivable," he demanded, "that I should in the course of time go for a few months without you?"

She smiled in her implacable splendour at his touching want of grasp. "Isn't the whole point that you can't *possibly* go for a few months? It would be a shame moreover if you did. I had quite as soon you went for a lifetime as for three days. I want you perfect, and three hours would prevent it. When I say ‹I want› you,» she handsomely developed, «I only mean I should want you if I had a right. My insanity, I quite understand, deprives me of all rights. But at the same time," she insisted, "you don't in the least undermine it by calling it a cold little theory. I don't pretend that it's anything else: my cold little theory is exactly indeed that it would be interesting to catch you—catch you young, as they say, since you *are* young—and put you through.»

He followed her with his face of gloom. "For the amusement of seeing what I should be at fifty?"

"There you are"—it had made her again quick; "and see what it is to be really intelligent! Precisely for the amusement, if you prefer that word—though I should use some other: save for the high idea, the intense interest, the peculiar beauty. I should see," said Mrs. Coyne, "what it makes of a man."

"You would indeed!" her visitor brooded.

She laughed out at his tone. "Ah but don't put it as a threat—as if you'd be Nick o' the Woods, and, to punish me for what I should have kept you from, wish to beat out my brains. You'd really be as pleased with me, I feel sure, as I should with you, and we'd grow old together in honour and patriotism." She became, however, the next moment braver; which had the effect of showing her as kinder. "It's all, when one considers, the fault of your peculiar situation—added, I mean, to the turn of your mind. The result of the combination of your starved state (which I call, you see, to oblige you, what you would call it) and your natural passion for everything old is as calculable as to-morrow's dawn," It was the sort of fact one could put in a nutshell. "The only way for you not to remain is not to go."

"You'll see whether I remain," Ralph said as drily as he could.

"Oh but do! Do," she earnestly repeated. "The great thing is after all not to spoil it—whichever way you take it; and isn't it also, when one thinks, much better you should be perfect for yourself than for me?"

"How you must, fortunately, hate and loathe me!"—Ralph returned to that with the same mastered misery. "Because if it weren't for that what a question for us to separate on!"

This appeared just to strike her. "It wouldn't be such a base one as you seem to suggest; but, to give you the benefit of the doubt, don't let us admit for a moment that it is the one! By which I mean that we *don›t* separate, inasmuch as for people to do that they must first have come together. For you to decline my condition I must first have imposed it. I mentioned just now,» she added for further lucidity, «the fact that makes you such a catch for one›s theory, but I didn't mention the other fact, the way you're in spite of everything pledged and committed—which spoils it all. The ideal subject of my experiment," she perfectly allowed, "needn't certainly be that particular rare bird, a young New Yorker who's an ardent student of history. It's over there," she appeared magnanimously to muse, "that history *can* best be studied!»

"How you laugh at me and lash me and rub it in!" Ralph grimly observed.

But she put the matter for him now as if in her achieved indulgence of it no misjudgment could interrupt her. "You've earned your holiday, and nothing can be more right and just than for it to be long and unclouded. I know nothing of a finer grace than the way you've gone on year after year doing without it for the charity nearest home; and I'm not so stupid as not to have a notion of the disadvantage at which, in the intellectual work you scraped time for, your limitations and privations must often have placed you. You did it, bravely and patiently, as you could, and I'm sure, ignorant as I am, that no one else could have in the conditions done it half so well. Only the conditions were so wrong that it's delightful they *can* at last be right. I›ll wait for another day,» she smiled, «to try my theory.»

"What you'll wait for," he after a moment returned, "is evidently and more especially another person."

She shook her head in general relinquishment. "Another person will never turn up. There will always be a flaw. If he's worth one's idea he'll be sure to have been over. If he hasn't been over he'll be sure not to be worth one's idea. *You*"—oh she could indeed, as he said, rub it in!— "would have been so perfectly worth it."

"Perhaps I might still try to be," he thoughtfully suggested, "if I could by any chance come as near to it as really to understand. But I assure you I don't so much as to take hold of it."

She struck him for a moment as on the point, in answer to this, of breaking into impatience and declaring that his failure of comprehension need't matter to him. He had a glimpse thus of what he believed—that she truly would have wished him to take her conception on trust, and, as it were, for the love of her;

to oblige her by adopting it, by accommodating himself blindly. Her courage, however, he made out, was insufficient for this, and the next minute she only did for herself what she could. "That's because I'm at the disadvantage, which I perfectly recognise, of not having practised what I preach—because I naturally, in my position, have everything against me." She smiled again for the vanity of the regret, but she went on. "If I could have known how I was now to feel I would never have gone."

Ralph tried to follow her as if something might come of it. "But it took nothing less than your charming experience, I gather, to produce your actual attitude. You would have had no attitude without it. You had to qualify yourself for your remonstrance."

He spoke so gravely that it made, in effect, for irony, and that in turn just visibly made her flinch. "Well, I do of course hold myself qualified, and of course I'm glad to be, on any terms. I give it to you at best as mere inevitable reaction, but the point I make is that as reaction it's final. One must choose at last"—she couldn't, he saw, but let herself go; "and I take up definitely with my own country. It's high time; here, *en fin de compte*, one can at least do or be something, show something, make something. To try and make something is at all events what's wanted of us, and even if we make nothing it's at least as good ta make it here on the spot as to go thousands of miles on as great a fool's errand. I want in short to be an American as other people are—well, whatever they are."

Ralph turned it all over. "Yes, it's the new cry, and what can be more interesting than to hear it sounded more or less in French? It's recommended—for the 'upper classes,' and perhaps even beginning a little to be tried by them. It wouldn't take much," he continued, "to make me say that the day only *could* inevitably come when it would be for its little hour the new pose."

"I dare say indeed it wouldn't take much to make you say it," she returned; "and I've also seen the moment coming at which—*for* the moment—you inevitably would. But I dare say you hold that the hour you speak of will pass: all the more reason therefore that I should make the most of it while it lasts. It may be only a dream, but the thing is—while one can—to keep dreaming."

He looked at her in silence longer than he had done yet. "What it comes to then is that you'll never dream of me."

"By no means; because it's just in dreams——!" But she pulled herself up. "I mean that their strangeness is their law. *They*, when they're happy, arrange everything to perfection. With you or without you at any rate," she pursued, "mine will go on. They'll be as fantastic as you please—that is as much about the poor product." She held him for a moment with this, then she broke out: "How shall we ever know his possibility unless we give him a chance? What I'm dying to see is the best we can turn out quite by ourselves."

He sacrificed his indifference. "The best young man?"

"Oh I don't care how old he is——"

"So long as he's young!" Poor Pendrel—for want of anything better to do—interrupted.

But she held her course. "The older he is the more he'll have given us time to see. Of course," she splendidly added, "he may be a failure, and, if he is, that will more or less settle the question. We're nowhere till it *is* settled.»

Ralph showed on his side no less noble a patience. "But isn't it settled by the cowboy?"

"The cowboy?" she stared.

"Why isn't he what you want, and why isn't he good enough? He sometimes in spite of his calling, I believe, lives to a great age. There are cases surely in which he will have given you time to see, and he has the great merit of standing there ready to your hand. You talk about the 'question,' but what is he but the best answer to it that any conditions at all conceivable can yield? You say mine—my conditions—are wrong; so that what are his, logically, unless right? If he isn't right *with* them it would seem therefore their fault. I wonder it doesn›t strike you in fine that if he isn›t good enough your idea itself perhaps isn›t.» Now that Ralph was launched he felt the tide high. «That›s what it comes to, your idea, dress it up as you will. You want a fellow only who shall have had adventures—and that, I hasten to grant, is any lady's right. There's no disputing about tastes, but that isn't true about principles. You want the adventure to have been, or necessarily to be, of the species most marked and determined by our climate, our geographical position, our political institutions, our social circumstances and our national character. It seems to me you see lines drawn remarkably sharp, but, allowing you that, I repeat that you strike me as having but to take your choice. The cow-boy," he suggested, "of middle-age, say——"

But she had now interrupted—as if for commiseration. "I don't even yet know what a cowboy is!"

It was at all events her seeing him gracelessly astray that she made him most feel. "There am *I* for you then. I don›t know what anyone is who leads the life of action—so little am I such a creature myself.» And straight—though he was sore for it—he looked the whole thing in the face. «It›s my type itself that's impossible to you. I shouldn't even here," he averred, "be able to meet your views or do what you require. I'd be a brute for it if I could—as indeed I often wish I *were* one; but I›ll be hanged if I see my way. My adventures are all in a very small circle"—and our young man tapped the seat of his brain. He thought it out at the moment almost as much for himself as for Aurora. "If it weren't that I'm trying to equip myself without disgrace in *this* one, I should doubt if in a fix of the kind that for you makes the hero I could be rightly counted on to know what to do. There you have me. Yes, it comes home to me: I only know what to do in thought or, as you might say, imagination—and but the least little bit even there; also without any firm confidence of doing it. So that if none but a ranchman need apply——!" he could in fine, while they dropped, with this, into their longest break, but look about for his hat. "I suppose it's no use my saying," he went on when he had found this article, "that if it interests you at all I may just possibly before long come in for something in England." He waited a little for her to take him up on it, but to the simple increase of his sense of her leaving him now to flounder as he would. He floundered accordingly an instant longer. "To me—to my mind of course I mean—such a windfall, in the shape of a bit of old property, an old house, a piece of suggestive concrete antiquity, easily represents, as you can conceive, rather a 'treat.' But I don't dream it's a thing to dazzle you with." He felt as soon as he had spoken, or rather as soon as her own silence had again marked itself, as if he had seen a vulgar bribe fall flat; and he was equally aware that what he next said deepened this appearance. "Of course there's nothing of that sort that can mean much to you to-day. You've seen everything again and again."

"Oh," she answered at last, "I've seen a great deal. But not what you will. You'll know so much better how. You've work cut out, but you're to be envied."

He put out his hand to her. "Good-bye—till next year."

For a moment she kept it. "Why do you talk so foolishly?"

"I say nothing more foolish than that I shall by that time see you again."

At this she slowly released him. "Of course it will be comparatively easy for you, but it won't really be worth your while to come back to spite me.

"I shall come back," said Ralph, "because I shall want to."

She had another of those weighted headshakes which, as if determined less from within than from without, suggested the perfect working of her beauty rather than that of her thought. "No—it's there that you're wrong and that I'm so right. I'm not such an idiot as not to know that there will always be a steamer and that you can always pay your passage. When I said that if you go you'll never come back I meant that you'll never wish to. Of course you can come back without wishing as much as you like. But that," she blandly remarked, "won't do for me."

"How well you know what I wish," he exhaled, "and how much every way you know about everything!"

"Well," she patiently replied before he had time finally to leave her, "it's not wholly my fault if an expression you once used to me has much worked in me. I remembered it as soon as I saw you to-day, and it would have made a folly of my talking to you of my conditions if I had done that with any other practical view than to call your attention to our impossibilities. You used it on one occasion when I was last at home in a way that has made me never forget it."

Ralph wondered. "I've used doubtless plenty of expressions and in plenty of absurd ways. But what in the world was this one?"

She brought it responsibly out. "'The sense of the past'."

He wondered still more. "Is that all?"

"You said it was the thing in life you desired most to arrive at, and that wherever you had found it—even where it was supposed to be most vivid and inspired—it had struck you as deplorably lacking intensity. At the intensity required, as you said, by any proper respect for itself, you proposed if possible yourself to arrive—art, research, curiosity, passion, the historic passion, as you called it, helping you. From that moment," she went on, "I saw. The sense of the past *is* your sense.»

He attended with a cold eye. "I haven't an idea what trash I may have talked."

"Don't be dishonest," she returned after a moment.

It brought, almost as a blow, a flush to his cheek. "Dishonest?"

"Don't deny yourself. Don't deny your ambition. Don't deny your genius."

He looked at her over it strangely, and then as if light had really broken, "Are *those* things what you hate me for?» he almost gasped.

"Live up to them," she returned as if she had not heard him. "You won't do anything else." She said it with a shortness that was almost stern, and he felt, detestably, as if she had but one moment instructed and at the other derided him. “Isn’t that moreover quite the lesson of the chance, the one you just mentioned, of what you may come in for? Isn’t an old property for you the very finger of fortune, the very ‘lead’ of providence? Profit for heaven’s sake by your old property. It will open your eyes.” She went on with widened looks which so further ennobled her face that they held him by themselves, standing out as he did from any truth in them. “That’s what your little book itself says—your little book that’s so wonderful for a man uninitiated; by which I venture to mean, you see, a man untravelled. It’s apropos of what you call the ‘backward vision,’ and I could immediately find the page. ‘There are particular places where things have happened, places enclosed and ordered and subject to the continuity of life mostly, that seem to put us into communication, and the spell is sometimes made to work by the imposition of hands, if it be patient enough, on an old object or an old surface.’ It’s very wonderful, you know, your having arrived at that, your having guessed it, in *this* place, which denies the old at every turn and contains so few such objects or surfaces.» So she continued to comment. “I hope your old house will contain plenty of them.”

Her quotation of this twaddle, as it struck him, from his small uninformed Essay, for which he now blushed, completed his disarray. Half a dozen things rose to his lips and stopped, but the bitterest got uttered. “What’s most extraordinary is that illusion I was under about your own type. I had taken it,” he explained, “as so beautifully suggestive.”

“Suggestive of what?” his hostess asked.

He looked at her without meeting this and as for the last time. “And again it’s all there. You would help me more than anyone. I feel it,” he continued with his eyes on her face, “really *not* as a mistake. Essentially—well, you›re one of them.»

“One of whom?”

“The women. *The* women. Good-bye,» he said again and offering his hand as if their queer chasm had been bridged by this intensity of the personal question. It was as if he took something that she couldn’t help giving, and what he took made him after an instant break out: “It will be you—I’ll be hanged!—who will come.”

But she was so firm and finished and high withal that even the ring of perception in this, or at least the rush of confidence, failed to make her wince. It only made her think to the very end of her goodnature. “I’ll tell you what I’ll do—if I can trust to your honour.”

“You can trust to my honour,” Pendrel said.

"Very well then, I promise you that if I find I want to—for that's the point—I'll loyally, bravely, and at whatever cost this time to my vanity, go back."

Pendrel weighed it. "Isn't there a danger that you'll take care *not* to find you want to?»

"Certainly a danger. I can do anything rather than want to. Anything, that is—I again promise you—short of marrying to save myself. It will take a miracle to move me, but if I *am* moved—moved from within and by something now incalculable—you may count on me. That," Aurora said, "is the meaning of my talking of my honour."

"And what's the meaning," Ralph asked, "of your talking of mine?"

"Why, that I take in the same way my chance of yours." She paused—he must understand.

This took him indeed no great time. "You'll have me if I do come?"

She hesitated again but an instant. "If you come on your honour. If you come——!" But it was as if she couldn't put it.

He tried to help her. "Without regret?"

Ah this wasn't good enough. "If you come with desire."

Ralph stared. "How in the world can I come without it if I come for you?"

She used again her large ease. "That won't help you if you're loyal."

"Loyal?" he wondered.

"To the real truth. To your genius."

"Oh I'll take care of my genius!"

"You will," she presently returned, "if you remember well this: that if you do rejoin me you engage to me to stay."

"Very good—I shall remember it well."

"Good-bye then," said Aurora Coyne.

She saw him to the door, where he paused for a last light. "Does that mean you hold you're safe?"

"It means that I hold you are," she answered as she turned away.

BOOK SECOND

It was not till he reached the street that he took in all she meant—as in particular by those last words. Without sense or sight, on leaving the house, he turned mechanically to the left and went blankly before him. This was not his way home, but he had no thought for ways. He moved simply because if he didn't there was nothing for him but to sit down on the first other doorstep. He felt mainly a great weakness—felt almost nothing else; yet it was a weakness that, oddly, sustained him for a long stretch, carried him up to the Park, determined his passing in, and then made him proceed unheedingly from the nearer to the further end. It was only on reaching the distant limit that he so much as noted a bench. The one he noted, however, he quickly sank upon; and little by little, thereafter, he gained a second consciousness. This was a perception of the beauty of the day, the mildest mood of March. The windless air, charged with spring, was like a brimming cup held still. The weather was divine, but the person supposed by him an hour before as dear to him as life had since then turned him out into the world. Well, the world was there to take him. Yes, he increasingly felt, he was there and his bench, placed near the top of the spread of a great alley, seemed to give him a general view of it. The object indeed after a while most distinct in this view was Ralph Pendrel himself, who rose there conspicuous and held our young friend's eyes. What marked him most was that he was a man humiliated. Arrange it as he would—or as *she* would—he had not been good enough. What it really came to—she might say what she liked—was that he was not of the type. Who *was* then?—he could but put himself the question. He even presently reflected that it might serve her right to find after a while there was nobody. Thus it was that Ralph Pendrel, with the world taking him, was yet thrown back on that gentleman. If he was not good enough for *her* he would be so for this alternative friend; and he gathered about him in thought for an hour all the merits he could muster. One of them precisely was that he had another and quite a different passion. He kept repeating to himself that just this, for his hard mistress, was his defect. He had wondered much before he got up whether he had it with such intensity as to constitute a vice—an inhuman side, that is, which she might pardonably distrust. The only thing for him doubtless now therefore would be to attest the intensity. He at last quitted the place with the step of a man proposing to test it on the spot. All this while, however, the anxiety truly deepest in him was about another affair. What in the world had happened to her in Europe?

It was when he reached the quiet scene which the recent lapse of his mother's soft pervasion had made so inconsequently, though now the abode of a more single state, not wider but narrower, that the next great thing befel him. He found on his table a letter from a firm of London solicitors, a communication on the face of it most harmoniously timed. It appeared that under the will of his late kinsman, Mr. Philip Augustus Pendrel, he inherited property—a fact enriched by the further mention, on the part of his informants, that should he find it convenient to come to England without undue delay his being on the spot would contribute to their action in his interest. It may immediately be said that the light wind of this stroke had even at the moment a happy effect on the heat of his wound. The event would certainly appeal with no great directness to the author of that injury, but its connection with the object of his other passion, as we have termed this source of inspiration, became at once of the liveliest. He made as rapidly as possible his arrangements for a journey to London, but he had time, before winding up the situation in New York, to hear from his cousin's representatives of matters still further concerning him and to receive from them in especial a letter addressed in that gentleman's hand and not at first found among his effects. It contained the only words that had, so far as he knew, come to any member of the American kinship, for two generations, from any member of the English. The English, he was perfectly aware, had been held by the American to be offish and haughty, and the American had stiffened itself to show that, since the question was of turning an unconscious back, the game was playable wherever backs were broad enough to show—which they made bold to feel themselves in the new country too. It was familiar to Ralph Pendrel that his father and his grandfather had fairly studied, and had practised with consistency, the art of the cold shoulder. They had each been more than once to England, but had "looked up" nobody and nothing—had clearly not acquainted themselves either by inquiry or closer visitation with those thin possibilities of something some day to their advantage, or to that of their posterity, that might have been dreamed of at the best. The property mainly accruing to Ralph loomed large now as a house—it was described as commodious—in a fine quarter of the town; this remained at first the limit of his charmed apprehension. No light, of the dimmest, had previously reached him as to the English view of what he had always heard called at home "the American attitude." He had in growing older not much believed there could be an English view; but it would seem after all that over this ground his fancy had too shyly hovered.

Mr. Pendrel's letter practically expressed the unsupposed quantity, and nothing surely could have been of more flattering effect. Written to be delivered after his death, it explained and enhanced, the delightful document—shaking the tree, as it were, for the golden fruit to fall. What it came to was that he had read as an old man his young relative's remarkable volume, "An Essay in Aid of the Reading of History," and, wishing somehow to testify to the admiration he felt for it, had come to consider that no symbol would be so solid as the old English house forming the sole item, in a long list of heavily hampered possessions, that he was free thus to dispose of. It was a mere town tenement, and none of the newest, but it was the best repayment of his debt he could make. He had nowhere seen the love of old things, of the scrutable, palpable past, nowhere felt an ear for stilled voices, as precious as they are faint, as seizable, truly, as they are fine, affirm a more remarkable power than in the pages that had moved him to gratitude. Unpretending though the title, the spare volume, but in which every word reached the mark, was a contribution to causes he had always had much at heart, a plea with which he rejoiced that the name of their family should have been associated. There were old things galore in Mansfield Square; the past, he considered, held its state there for those with the wit to make it out; and, should his young kinsman accept his bequest, he would find himself master of a scene in which a chapter of history—obscure, though not so remote as might perhaps have been wished—would perhaps by his intervention step more into the light. The generations at least had passed through it, clinging indeed as long as they might, and couldn't have failed to leave something of their mark, which it would doubtless interest Mr. Ralph to puzzle out. It was the testator's wish that he should do so at his ease. The letter in fine was, as Ralph said, a deucedly beautiful gentlemanly one, and the turn of the wheel of fortune. The material advantage might be uncertain; but it was blessedly not for the economic question, it was for the historic, the aesthetic, fairly in fact for the cryptic, that he cared. A big London house sounded in truth on the face of the matter less like an aid to research than like an exposure to rates and taxes, a legacy of the order vulgarly known as thumping. But verily too even London, for our rare young man, was within the pale of romance. His "other" passion in short had soon begun freshly to glow.

Within a month it had shaken him still harder, and all the more that, this time, his impatience had fallen and two or three of his illusions with it: his curiosity had sat down to its feast. He had encountered in London more business than he expected, but had not encountered what he most feared, the display of a swarm of litigants. This greatly eased his mind, since if injustice had been done it would have taken much from the savour of the feast. There was no nearer relative, it surprisingly seemed, no counter-claimant, no hint in the air of a satisfaction disputed. No unfortunate and expropriated person came, in a word, to light, and there was therefore neither a cause to defend nor a sacrifice to consider. The only thing really to consider in such a stroke of luck was its violation of the common law of prose. Life was at best good prose—when it wasn't bad; and Mr. Pendrel's succession was—all "town tenement" as it might be—poetry undefiled. It was none the less poetry that the value of the property was so easily ascertained to be high. Ralph reflected not even for a moment after he had been to see it that a fine country estate would have been more to his purpose. He *had* no purpose, he freely recognised, but to begin at once to cultivate whatever relation should seem most fruitful to his so suddenly acquired "stake" in an alien order. The circumstance of its being exactly what it was—of no greater extent, yet of no less dignity—ministered beyond anything else for the new master to a sense of close communication with the old. It was extraordinary how on this ground the young man felt himself understood; and he reflected endlessly as well as amazedly on the fact that it had all been done for him by his slim composition of five years before, so timid, so futile in the light of his subsequent growth. The affair would have been less of a fairytale—and had indeed thereby less of a charm—if Mr. Pendrel's impulse had been determined by such a book as he might now write. What a book, what books, moreover, should properly proceed, he said to himself, from a longer and nearer view of the silent secrets of the place! *These* were what had been bequeathed him, these were what the hand of death had placed before him, on the table, as in a locked brass-bound box the key of which he was to find. It would not be by any weakness of his, please God, that a single one of them should fail of its message.

He liked to think, as he took possession, that his kinsman was watching, and therewith waiting, beyond the grave; though the way he had abstained from restrictive conditions—from all, that is, save a single one hereafter to be mentioned—was perhaps the deepest note in his good taste. The part played in the whole business by that happy principle was in truth at moments almost such as to make poor Ralph uneasy. There was a roundness in his fortune that might seem too much to beguile. Were blessings so unexpected ever, beyond a certain point, anything but traps? Should he begin to make his way into the secrets, as they hovered and hung there, wearing a sort of sensible consistency, who could say where he might come out, into what dark deeps of knowledge he might be drawn, or how he should "like," given what must perhaps at the best stick to him of insuperable modern prejudice, the face of some of his discoveries? He encountered however on this ground of a possible menace to his peace a reassurance that sprang, and with all eagerness, from the very nature of his mind. He lived, so far as a wit sharpened by friction with the real permitted him, in his imagination; but if life was for this faculty but a chain of open doors through which endless connections danced there was yet no knowledge in the world on which one should wish a door closed. There was none at any rate that in the glow of his first impression of his property he didn't desire much more to face than to shirk. If he was even in this early stage a little disconcerted it came only from the too narrow limits in which Mr. Pendrel's personal image, meeting his mind's eye at odd moments on the spot and constantly invoked by his gratitude, appeared to have arranged to reveal itself. He would have been particularly grateful for a portrait; but though there were in the house other framed physiognomies these were things—and not unluckily either!—of a different order of reference, an order in which the friendly photograph for instance, whether of the late tenant of the place or of any other subject, played no part. The friendly photograph had been with us for half a century, but there was nothing there to Ralph's vision so new as that. Number Nine Mansfield Square affected that vision, in short, to a degree presently to be explained, as with an inimitable reserve in respect to the modern world. It had crossed the threshold of the century, the nineteenth, it had even measured a few steps of the portentous prospect, but where it had stopped, pulled up very short and as with its head in the air—it had stopped, one might have surmised, with a kind of disgust. It had determined clearly, on the apprehension then interchanged, to have as little to say to the future as an animated home, of whatever period, might get off with. "And yet I am the future," Ralph Pendrel mused, "and I dream of making it speak."

Face to face with it then, when he felt that already and quite distinctly it was speaking—which happened the first time that ever, key in hand, he was able to enter it unaccompanied—there was an inconsequence to note, and one from which he drew a fine pleasure. He was thus moved more shrewdly to reflect that if he was so trusted there must have been something in him to inspire it. Was he to such a tune the future? Had not his taste for "research," which was more personally his passion for the past, worked rather, and despite his comparative youth, to transmute him? On the day he disembarked in England he felt himself as never before ranged in that interest, counted on that side of the line. It was to this he had been brought by his desire to remount the stream of time, really to bathe in its upper and more natural waters, to risk even, as he might say, drinking of them. No man, he well believed, could ever so much have wanted to look behind and still behind—to scale the high wall into which the successive years, each a squared block, pile themselves in our rear and look over as nearly as possible with the eye of sense into, unless it should rather be called out of, the vast prison yard. He was by the turn of his spirit oddly indifferent to the actual and the possible; his interest was all in the spent and the displaced, in what had been determined and composed roundabout him, what had been presented as a subject and a picture, by ceasing—so far as things ever cease—to bustle or even to be. It was when life was framed in death that the picture was really hung up. If his idea in fine was to recover the lost moment, to feel the stopped pulse, it was to do so as experience, in order to be again consciously the creature that had been, to breathe as he had breathed and feel the pressure that he had felt. The truth most involved for him, so intent, in the insistent ardour of the artist, was that art was capable of an energy to this end never yet to all appearance fully required of it. With an address less awkward, a wooing less shy, an embrace less weak, it would draw the foregone much closer to its breast. What he wanted himself was the very smell of that simpler mixture of things that had so long served; he wanted the very tick of the old stopped clocks. He wanted the hour of the day at which this and that had happened, and the temperature and the weather and the sound, and yet more the stillness, from the street, and the exact look-out, with the corresponding look-in, through the window and the slant on the walls of the light of afternoons that had been. He wanted the unimaginable accidents, the little notes of truth for which the common lens of history, however the scowling muse might bury her nose, was not sufficiently fine. He wanted evidence of a sort for which there had never been documents enough, or for which documents mainly, however multiplied, would never *be* enough. That was indeed in any case the artist›s method—to try for an ell in order to get an inch. The difficult, as at best it is, becomes under such conditions so dire that to face it with any prospect one had to propose the impossible. Recovering the lost was at all events on this scale much like entering the enemy's lines to get back one's dead for burial; and to that extent was he not, by his deepening penetration, contemporaneous and present? "Present" was a word used by him in a sense of his own and meaning as regards most things about him markedly absent. It was for the old ghosts to take him for one of themselves.

The spirit of gossip governed but little, he had promptly seen, the commerce of his friends the London solicitors with their clients; they were persons of a hard professional and facial surface and of settled dull complexion, giving back, on a rap of the knuckle, the special sharp answer, but not thereby corrupted to any human resonance. They betrayed to him in consequence few of Mr. Pendrel's secrets, and he shrank on his side from giving the measure of his ignorance of the source of so large a bounty. This was perhaps the weakness of a slightly lame pride; he had not been too proud to accept, but he felt that in asking many questions he should show himself indebted to a stranger. He accordingly made out little more than that his kinsman had read books, possibly even pursued studies and entertained ideals, had had another habitation, the estate of Driffle, in the country, much more frequented, and had never, since forming, on the occasion of an inheritance in the maternal line, the connection with Mansfield Square, been disposed to pass in London—it was even a little odd—more than two or three weeks together. Odder still, though to our young man's but half informed view, was it that his visits to town appeared to have been almost always of the autumn and the winter, had indeed often taken place at Christmas and at Easter, the periods, by the rigid London law, of gregarious intermission. He had been a person, it was clear, of few commonplace conformities, a person with a fine sense for his own taste and his own freedom, one in whose life the accents, as who should say, were not placed where people in general place them. There were moreover in the history points of indistinctness which would doubtless clear up under pressure; as the fact for instance that though he had entered into possession in middle life he had yet affirmed this possession so thoroughly that confusion and a grey vagueness had already settled on the memory of whatever predecessors, who seemed to lurk indistinguishable behind him. At the same time that he had loved and guarded the place, he had none the less, as might have been remarked and as was somehow to be divined, not admitted it to the last familiarity. This went so far as to suggest that in keeping it clear and inviolate he had had in view betimes the convenience of some other considerable person.

That beneficiary, in the form of his American cousin, so rejoiced in such an inference that, during the first few days, he hung about under cover of night, and with mingled diffidence and pride, before the inexpressive front. The pride was for all he was already aware of within, while the diffidence was for the caretaker and her husband, a mature and obese but irreproachably formal policeman—persons of high respectability both, placed in charge by Mr. Pendrel's executors, to whom he feared to show as frivolous in knocking yet again. Was he *not* for that matter frivolous actually and sufficiently, he more than once asked himself, carried off his intellectual feet to such a point by an accident that would have had for most people a mere relation to their income? He was conscious enough that what had thus caught him up to flights of fancy was an object of a class more definable than almost any other as of the reverse of extraordinary, a London house of the elder, larger, finer type, of an age long anterior to the age of jerry-building, but still after all a mere grey square section of a street, passed and repassed by cabs and costermongers, called at by the milkman, numbered by the vestryman, and marked by the solicitude of this last functionary to the extent exactly of an unimpressive street-lamp placed straight, or rather in fact placed considerably crooked, before the door. The street-lamp was a disfavour to the dark backward into which Ralph loved to look, and yet he was perhaps a little glad of its presence on the two or three occasions just mentioned—occasions of his patrolling the opposite side in covert contemplation. The dusky front at these times showed its eyes—admirable many-paned windows, at once markedly numerous and markedly interspaced—in a manner more responsive to his own. He had moments of stopping when the coast was clear for a longer stare and then of going on in pronounced detachment at the approach of observation. There was still a want of ease in his ecstasy, if it were not rather that the very essence of the ecstasy was a certain depth of apprehension.

If as he paced he sought to avoid suspicion, of what was it at bottom that he was to have been suspected? He would have confessed, had the question been put to him, that it was only of his thoughts, which he was himself moreover the only person to know anything about. If he desired so extremely to hide them was it then that his conscience was bad about them? An examination of the state of his conscience would perhaps in truth have shown him as entertaining a hope scarce seriously to be confessed. If he had an underhand dream that his house might prove "haunted"—the result of an inordinate conception, in his previous time, of old and doubtless foolish tales—the thing might after all have been forgiven to his so belated freedom. Experience had lagged with him behind interpretation, and the worst that could have been said was that his gift for the latter might do well to pause awhile till an increase of the former could catch up. By the time it did catch up he might perhaps have come to make out for himself that, as is perfectly known to biases millions, despair seldom fails to settle on any surmise that the common forces of solicitation in respectable neighbourhoods may be in a given case much transcended. He was sufficiently a man of the world, further, not to care to face the smile that would greet his having had that lesson to learn. He had disembarked with an immense provision of prepared sensibility, but had packed into its interstices various fine precautions against his passing for a fool. He was slightly ashamed, if the truth be told, of the bounds he had honestly to set to his reach of reminiscence, and he understood that he should most please himself by making his pretensions few. It would be simple enough, he seemed to see, to betray on occasion his ignorance, but he might find it in general awkward to betray some sides of his knowledge. He knew too much for a man who had seen so little, and nothing could be more fatuous than to go about apologising. Of course he exaggerated the danger of the perception of either excess in so preoccupied a world. He was at any rate careful to keep to himself his real reason for disgustedly flushing in hours of privacy at the thought of the figure his acquisition would make at the hands, or at least under the pen, of auctioneers and agents eager to invite him to regard it as a source of income. The reason was simply that the language of advertisement, the inimitable catchpenny flourish, depressed him by the perfection of its missing of the whole point. The whole point, that of the exceptional eligibility they panted to express in their terms, was the ineffable genius itself of the place, which while he kept indirectly raking it, grew upon him day by day. He couldn't go so far as to tell anyone that he had never seen anything so old—so old at once and so elaborate—as a structure dating only from the earlier years of the previous century. He couldn't decently cry it on the housetops that he had never yet so wetted his lips at the founts of romance. It was indeed without doubt, as he reflected, in favour of one's not finding people laugh in one's face that he happened to be in general little addicted to crying from the housetops.

Just these high considerations were in all probability the influence most active in his attitude toward the only approach to an adverse interest with which he was to perceive himself confronted. It had been at their first interview made known to him by his kinsman's main representative that the house stood, for the time, subject to a short lease—a lease for the "season" given by its late proprietor, apparently in one of his rare fits of response to the economic motive, the previous year; which arrangement constituted in fact but the renewal of an understanding arrived at, on more than one other occasion, in the same conditions. The tenant bequeathed by Mr. Pendrel to his successor had in other words already three times enjoyed the tenancy, and though it was not impossible the agreement might be amicably rescinded it was for this successor to judge whether he preferred to sacrifice so substantial a gain. The gain, Ralph understood, was of a round weekly sum, as to the weight of which in the scale he reserved his decision. He had a general wish not to begin by a failure to oblige, as well, positively quite at first, as an imperfect, almost a deprecatory, sense of possession. It pulled him up a little on the other hand, after he had seen the place, to think of prior possession, so far as he was concerned, insisted on and enjoyed by a parcel of people whose very name was new to him. Mrs. Midmore of Drydown in Hampshire embodied the claim with which he had to reckon, but he knew little of Mrs. Midmore, save that she had, with her address, as his firm of friends called it, rather an old-time imaging sound. It was judiciously remarked by the firm that she was of a family with which Mr. Pendrel's relations appeared, so far as they were traceable, to have been close; and moreover that some such tradition was needed to account for his departure from a custom of indifference to the pecuniary argument so patent in other connections. Except in these instances the house had practically never been let—within, as might be said, the modern era. It might be even now, as was hinted to Ralph, offered at a much higher figure than the rental subscribed to by Mrs. Midmore. This last little fact it really was that had in its perverse operation most weight with our young man. Full of scruples and refinements and of the clash of cross-lights in which he saw things, he knew the arrangement would have troubled him more had a handsomer bargain been made for him. If he accepted at all the necessity of trafficking in his treasure it was a salve to discomfort that the traffic was poor.

By the time he solemnly entered it had been further mentioned to him that the lady's appreciation of the place—unless its appeal were more especially to her son, or to one or other, if not both, of her two daughters—had been noted as almost extravagant. Signs in short had not been wanting of the length to which such an attachment could go. Poor Ralph at the end of an hour indeed would have understood any length; but it was under this impression precisely that he fell into a train of delays. The immediate effect of his first visit had been the wish to "move in" that afternoon; the next had been a gathering doubt as to whether he had better do so at all. The inner scene spoke to him with a hundred voices, yet not one of these phrased to him quite happily the terms of the single life there. The strangest part of this moreover was that his hesitation—which fairly partook of the nature of a sort of sacred terror—rested not in the least on any vision of what was wanting, but wholly on the consciousness, almost as strong as a shock, of what was impressively, what was tremendously, involved. He tried to put it to himself simply, yet was not sure he put it sincerely, in pronouncing it impossible he should fill out so many rooms. He apprehended at bottom what might be going to happen—his making up his mind on some uncandid basis that temporary lodgings elsewhere were his indicated course. The want of candour would lie in the plea of absurdity—the absurdity of his organising, with so much else to do, such an establishment as would consort with such a setting. It would be swagger, it would be vulgar precipitate eagerness, he on the one side reasoned, to waste time in the pretence of really "running" such a place; and there would be on the other a distinct offence in attempting to inhabit it meanly. He should have time enough to ask himself what would have been his benefactor's idea. The idea would come to him in some way of its own: evidently it had been thrown out in the offered facts themselves; they held it there in reserve and in subtle solution. On its appearing he should know it, and he mustn't before that make a mistake.

This was meanwhile in the interest of all the things for which in his queer position he wanted a free hand. His queer position was that, as he privately panted, everything had dropped on him at once. He saw the face of Aurora Coyne whenever he winced with one of those livelier throbs of the sense of "Europe" which had begun to consume him even before his ship sighted land. He had sniffed the elder world from afar very much as Columbus had caught on his immortal approach the spices of the Western Isles. His consciousness was deep and confused, but "Europe" was for the time and for convenience the sign easiest to know it by. It hovered before him, this sign, in places as to which signs were mainly of another sort; on his dusty Liverpool dock, in his rattling train to Euston, when he called, betimes, on the Clifford Street tailor recommended to him, when he helped himself at his "private hotel" from the inveterate muffin-plate that protected at breakfast the tepidity of his slop-bowl, and when he swayed, aloft, with the movement of the bus that brought him back through historic ways from his prime pilgrimage to the City. It scarce took even the bus to make him sway; he was at the mercy, wherever he found himself and to whatever he clung, of such incalculable gusts. This was what he meant by his almost scared consciousness of the simultaneous and the many. He had first of all his base arrears to make up, after which he could settle with his special relation. He gasped on reminding himself as his tenth day dawned that the glimpse accompanied for him with so much ado was yet but a small millionth of the whole. The whole waited, for didn't there hang behind this troublous foreground the vast vagueness which the English themselves spoke of as "abroad"? Ah he was in all conscience already abroad enough!

It was on the morning of this tenth day that he definitely promised his friends in the City the expression on the morrow of his final view of Mrs. Midmore. He had hung the night before, again postponing re-entrance, in front of the habitation contingently reserved for her, and he had now returned westward with a certain gathered and penitent sharpness on the subject of action. Action would be to drive straight to Mansfield Square, indulge himself with another impression, let this impression settle the case and then wire to the City the result of it. It so befell none the less that he repaired again—and as if mechanically and in the beguiling intensity of this conclusion—to his lodgings, where, instead of taking, after a glance at some letters that had come in, a prompt fresh start, he dropped into a chair and drew it a foot or two nearer the fire that a particularly English April seemed huskily to have prescribed. The day was dark and damp, and it had suddenly occurred to him that not once yet, since the hour, at home, of his sombre station in the Park, had he so much as stopped to think. He had in very fact, as we make out, not stopped thinking, for what had it been but thought that drove him on and kept him going?—the thought of all the use he should have for the abounding fruits of a larger perception, the thought of the really wonderful book, as it would be this time, that he foresaw himself writing. That was as far as he had got with the book, of which the plan still remained sketchy; he prefigured it mainly as a volume that should "count"—which meant for him to be noticed by the half-dozen persons who themselves counted and who would more or less understand. He had already, and even repeatedly, asked himself when he should be able so to detach himself as to think at all straight about his book; detachment and selection, prime aids of the artist, were the sacred sparenesses menaced by a rank growth of material. It was perhaps the better to think that he now put back his head and closed his eyes; he at any rate considered to such purpose that he never moved for two hours. The first conception his mind had registered was that he was brutally tired. When he woke the day was darker, and on shaking himself for a look from his window he was met by a state of rain. Wet, muddy, ugly, the spring afternoon offered nothing of its own and seemed to mark a general break of the spells it had hitherto helped to work. Number Nine, from beyond its interposing spread of splashy crossings, faced him for the first time without its high authority. But this note of the hour soon determined him only the more: if he had in fact let too fresh a fancy run away with him it positively concerned his self-respect that the extravagance should cease. There was a question in a word to clear up—a question sufficiently identical, moreover, with the other and immediate one, the one he must no longer leave open. He signed from where he stood to a passing hansom, and in a few minutes was rolling, with the glass down, toward Mansfield Square. It was an occasion at last on which he could lift with assurance the knocker he hadn't once even yet taken a proprietor's full liberty with—an engine huge, heavy, ancient, brazen, polished, essentially defiant of any trifling, but now resoundingly applied.

It was the merit of the good couple in charge that they at least let him alone, and he had at present more than ever a sense, not unembroidered by fond prejudice, of the figure he made for them, of which it harmlessly amused him to think. It agreed with he knew not what interior ancientry and was truly but part of the deep picture that had already drawn him into a bottomless abyss of "tone" whenever the high door closed behind him and he stood with his sharp special thrill in the wide white hall, which he had from the first noted with rapture as paved in alternate squares of white marble and black, each so old that the white was worn nearly to yellow and the black nearly to blue. He had never for an instant doubted of the virtue, the value he would have called it in his esoteric sense, of this particular spot; which had originally given him, on the instant, under his first flush, the measure of a possible experience. He had said to himself crudely and artlessly "It's Jacobean"—which it wasn't, even though he had thought but of the later James. The intensity of the inference and the charm of the mistake had marked withal his good faith; the memory of which was to remind him later on of how everything still to come was then latent in that plot of space, and of how everything that *had*, was accorded and attested by it. The door to-day had but once more to close with the slight heaviness that inevitably defeated discretion and the overpaid and dismissed hansom to be heard for a minute get again into empty motion on the other side of it, for Ralph to feel at ease about the lapsed influence he had come to start up. The influence was on this occasion not only all there—it was really there as it had been on no other. His friends in charge, effacing themselves and leaving him to roam, appeared literally to have provided the particular hush into which it would best step forth, and he liked to figure them as types of ancient servitude, quaint and knowing their place, properly awestruck by the outland gentleman who had suddenly become the providence of their compact round world. It was a world clearly that they desired to remain shut up in, and a happy instinct had admonished them that they best appeased fortune by holding their breath. They could scarce have done better had they known of spells and superstitions and been possessed with a recipe for causing them to flourish. They even stayed downstairs too consistently to give their new patron his chance of expressing to them how honestly he judged them to keep his house.

That was what struck him afresh after he had mounted the large old stair and begun to pass from room to room: there was something in his impression so indefinably prepared by other hands that acknowledgment surely ought somehow and somewhere to be made. It all came back of course soon enough to thanking Mr. Pendrel, and this in truth Ralph sufficiently did by his mere attitude from point to point. That was the question on the whole as to which he was easiest; wherever he paused to draw a long breath and again look round he felt his gratitude carry and his appreciation in a singular degree picked up and noted. Not yet for that matter had it so affected him this evening as returning richly upon himself. The cold rain was on his window-pane, and it damped the great London hum. These squares of old glass were small and many and the frames that enclosed them thick; the appropriate recess, of which no window failed, was deep, and Ralph could as he looked out rest a knee on the flat cushion, all flowered and faded, that covered the solid bench. He looked out only to look in again under the charm of isolation and enclosure, of being separated from the splashed Square and its blurred and distant life much more by time than by space; under the charm above all of the queer incomparable London light—unless one frankly loved it rather as London shade—which he had repeatedly noted as so strange as to be at its finest sinister, and which just now scattered as never before its air over what surrounded him. However else this air might have been described it was signally not the light of freshness and suggested as little as possible the element in which the first children of nature might have begun to take notice. Ages, generations, inventions, corruptions had produced it, and it seemed, wherever it rested, to have filtered through the bed of history. It made the objects about show for the time as in something "turned on"—something highly successful that he might have seen at the theatre. What was one to call the confounding impression but that of some stamp, some deposit again laid bare, of a conscious past, recognising no less than recognised?

This was a character to which every item involved in Mr. Pendrel's bequest quite naturally and directly contributed. They were all items of duration and evidence, all smoothed with service and charged with accumulated messages. The house was of about 1710, and nothing of that age had ever spoken of it to Ralph in such a tone of having dropped nothing by the way to reach him.

Large, simple and straight, effective from a happy relation of line to line and space to space, from a dignity that seemed somehow a product of rightnesses even as an effect in arithmetic is a concord of numbers, it was exemplary in its kind, and its kind was for its new master the kind with which he could least imagine ever having a quarrel. The type carried him back and back till he remembered that such offices were solemn for honours after all not rare; yet at the same time that he tasted the sweet staleness almost to intoxication he rejoiced in the fact that the animating presences, all the other figures involved, could still be fitted together. They were of an age so remote and yet of an imagery so near. None of the steps were missing and the backward journey took no turns. It wasn't for Ralph as if he had lost himself, as he might have done in a deeper abyss, but much rather as if in respect to what he most cared for he had never found himself till now. As the house was his house, so the time, as it sank into him, was his time. It sank into him as he sat in the handsome chairs, specimens surely of price, as he figured the fineness of inlaid tables, rejoicing in the form of panels and pilasters and pronouncing the whole scene inimitably "quiet." It had never been either overloaded or despoiled; everything was in place and answered and acted; the large clear rooms almost furnished themselves, moreover, thanks to pleasant proportion and surface, without the aid of redundancy. He gave himself with relief, with gratitude for their luck, to all they had escaped knowing, all that, in the vulgarest of ages, they had succeeded in not inheriting. There wasn't a chimney-piece, an arched recess, a glazed and columned cupboard, that hadn't for our young man the note of structural style, not a cornice nor a moulding that his eye didn't softly brush, not a sunk glass, above a shelf, unevenly bevelled and however tarnished, in which shadows didn't condense themselves into shapes, not an old hinge nor an old brass lock that he couldn't work with love of the act, not an echo on the great stairs—he had from the first classed the staircase as "great"—that he didn't each time pause to catch again. He drew himself along the banister like a schoolboy yearning for a slide; all the more that the banister of hammered iron, admirably flourished and scalloped and with a handrail of polished oak, vaguely commended itself to him as French and matchable in an old Paris *hôtel.* A museum the place on this occasion more than ever became, but a museum of held reverberations still more than of kept specimens. It contained more of these latter than his fondest dream had originally pleaded for, but he felt at moments that even had they all been absent the sense of the whole would have been scarce less saved or the composition less happy. The walls and windows and floors sufficiently produced the effect—the perfect "state" of everything sufficiently sounded the note.

There were questions—more even than he could meet—that came up for him in the act of absence; but these questions either practically answered themselves by contact, or, so far as they didn't, merged themselves in others to which the answers might wait. Had the array of appurtenances, such as it was, been there from of old, or were they objects got together with the modern motive and precisely for the sake of their suggestion? Did they in their elegant sparseness render the house technically "furnished," and could it in point of fact be lived in without additions and excrescences that would make it wrong? Were the things honest rarities such as collectors would jump at, or only a fortuitous handful that roughly and loosely harmonised? How came it that if they were really "good" they were not on everyone's tongue, and how above all that if they were poor they so convinced and beguiled? These would have been matters to clear up by putting them to the test, and Ralph knew of more ways than one in which, should he ask for an hour from an obliging expert, his eyes would probably open. But experts and tests were, as it happened, and as I have already signified, quite what he was as yet least moved to cultivate; his instinct, with so much more on his consciousness, from the first concussion, than he could fairly handle, having been all to postpone the social complication, the presentation of letters, the looking up of friends. It had struck him that, marked out by his odd fate for an hospitality so rare and so special, he might temporarily neglect any minor appeal. There was already before him, goodness knew, matter enough for response.

This evening at any rate, while the day darkened and the weather shrouded his vigil, he invoked convenient illusions with a tremour he had not yet felt; he arrived, between his fondness and his fear, at the easiest compromise with concentration. Unmistakeably, as the afternoon waned, he held off as much as he hovered. It was a natural effect of his restlessness that he didn't for the present see himself settled. It was positively as if, with the cup so held to his lips, the taste of 1710 might prove too stiff a dose. He would judge, as it were, when he came back—back, as who should say also, from everywhere else. He would go of course everywhere else; intellectually now he could so well afford to. This would make all the general initiation that, as a preliminary, was indispensable—the series of scattered dashes and superficial dips. Strange his divination, or whatever one might call it, that from such a plunge at Number Nine as would thoroughly penetrate he might possibly not emerge undamaged—or even, it was actually to be figured, not emerge at all. He might remain there below, remain in the quintessential depth that stood so ready for a real resident. He pulled up his patrol as it again came to him that for this privilege of real residence he had a candidate in hand. He loitered anew, looked and listened, strolled and stopped, paused at moments, with hands in pockets, to gaze all too gravely at a mere panel in a wainscot, a mere seam in a curtain, and repeat over vaguely the name of Mrs. Midmore of Drydown. She had gradually become for him less abstract, and he reflected with interest that she was the one historic figure he was as yet in position to introduce into the view. There were in fact moments of desultory thought when he felt as if she were already in it by her own act—so close a relation to it seemed asserted by her proved resolution. This proved resolution was, so far as his wondering mind could now place her before him, what was most the mark of her aspect, and there were literally for him flights of fancy through which, as she stood there, she looked out at him with a hard old face. Yes, she would be old, Mrs. Midmore of Drydown—in the sense at least that she wouldn't be new: she wouldn't without that have what he could only phrase as the connection; and she would not less assuredly be hard: she wouldn't without that have what he could only think of as the nerve. He dressed her, with unwitting confusion, in the old manner of the house—the manner of the two or three portraits of women (these, alas, plainly enough, not from illustrious or even from known hands) inserted in the woodwork of the reception rooms, he heard for an instant, hallucinated, the scrape of her stiff petticoat on the floor, and the tap of her shoes, if it weren't rather the click of her small crutch, on the stone stair. She wore a little black hood fastened under her chin by an ornament—*that* old-time trinket would be priceless of a truth; and her pronunciation of certain words made her, as she talked, difficult to understand. Could she, he wistfully wondered, live in the house as it stood?—it being, as might have been made out, a puzzle to him to see her there so poorly convenienced, and yet not less a pain to equip her with a background of cosy corners or photographs framed in leather, of tailor-made ladies doing tricks with little dogs and gentlemen in tweed mixtures tilting back "good" chairs.

The few portraits of men in the house were not sensibly superior to the three or four women's, besides being, in a couple of cases, of a date observably later; but they had alike that prime and sufficient property of the old portrait—they had, as Ralph put it to himself, their more or less attaching "look" to give out. They had in short those painted eyes for the particular purpose of following their friend as he moved; and one of the things he actually found himself most doing was to circulate in their presence just to see for his amusement how far they would in this fashion go. They all had somehow the art of going further than he had ever perceived such a company—on the walls of a museum for instance—to coincide in going. His amusements, it will be noted, were for a rainy hour simple enough, and a protected observer of some of his proceedings would doubtless have pronounced them pointless to the verge of puerility. This, however, would result partly from the difficulty of his making a lucid plea for what all the while took place within him. It was a ferment deep enough—even while he might superficially have appeared but to be asking the flat framed images what *they* thought of the question of his admitting Mrs. Midmore. He read into them as he lingered before them the knowledge of her being of their company; they had had on occasion, it would seem, to live with her, they had witnessed her ways and could give him the answer he watched and waited for. Nothing could have been more amusing, if, always, he was amused—than his impression at once that they really gave it and that he yet quite as really couldn't make it out. Portraits of the dead are at best ironic things, but, unknown and unnamed as were these victims of fate, none had ever so affected him as after all reacting upon it. This general innuendo, as he felt himself take it from them, was quite out of scale with their general obscurity. It represented none the less for his question neither a yea nor a nay; though it might have made one or the other if he could only have told which. It was thus their character, excepting only one, that they defied interpretation, and the character of the exception scarce bettered the case.

In presence of the single picture in which anything to call art had been appreciably active Ralph was luckily able—from the point of view of diversion—to treat himself to the sense of something like a prodigy. Let into the upper wainscot of the innermost and smallest of the three drawing-rooms, a charming panelled parlour lighted from the large walled court behind the house, which made a decent distance for other roofs, chimneys and windows, this work, prominent in its place over the mantel, depicted a personage who simply appeared to have sought to ignore our friend's appeal by turning away his face. This it was that constituted the prodigy, for Ralph had truly never seen a gentleman painted, and painted beautifully, in so thankless a posture. It gave the figure a conscious air which might have made for ridicule had it not so positively made for life; whereby to laugh at it would verily have been, in spite of its averted look, too much like laughing in a gentleman's face. The gentleman in question here had turned his back, and for all the world as if he had turned it within the picture. This of course was far from the first time Ralph had admired and studied him, but it was the first time of his finding his attention throb with the idea that the actual attitude might change—that it had even probably, that it had in fact repeatedly, done so. Extravagant enough such an imagination, but now settling on our young man in force—the prodigy that when one wasn't there the figure looked as figures in portraits inveterately look, somewhere into the room, and that this miraculous shift, the concealment of feature and identity, took place only when one's step drew near. Who in the world had ever "sat"—though in point of fact the model in this case stood—in a position that so trifled with the question of resemblance? The only explanation conceivable was some motive on the sitter's part—since it surely wouldn't have been on the artist's—for wishing resemblance minimised; a situation in which a refusal to sit at all would have been a much easier course. From the first occasion of his pausing there Ralph Pendrel had spun his fine thread, matching the wilful position with this and that hypothesis; only not till now had his view of the possible taken this monstrous jump. He had read into the picture the notion of a wager, a joke, or even of some particular vanity as to poise of head, form of ear, shape of shoulder, or even fit of coat, some whim of old-time elegance, some conceit of the age of the bucks—among whom, not indistinguishably, the original of the portrait might have figured. Had he otherwise, failing these possibilities, a face to be so deprecated, a face so inferior to the rest of his person as to constitute a deformity prohibitive or represent an identity in some way compromised? There was nothing Ralph had in fine been able to think of that was not more or less met by the objection that an easier choice is usually open to the afflicted and the dishonoured.

The honours were exactly what this representation in a high degree enjoyed; for if it had not been placed in the largest and best room it had claimed, still better, a room all to itself. The little innermost parlour was moreover for its new proprietor the most consecrated corner of the house. It was there that, as he had repeatedly said to himself, the spell worked best; it was there, for instance, that, as he was perfectly sure, Mrs. Midmore of Drydown would like best to sit; but didn't it by the same token precisely happen that the absence of another portrait was what would permit the fullest license within the frame to the subject of this one? He might turn about as he liked when he didn't turn before other eyes. When once this conceit of his turning had lodged itself in Pendrel's brain the way our friend played with it would have exposed him perhaps more than anything else—had there been observation of him too—to that charge of apparent levity which we have rejoiced for him that there was no one to bring. He came and went, passed into the next room and then returned quickly, presented his own back to the chimney-piece and wheeled round on a sudden—all as if he might have caught his mystificator bringing off the trick.

No other trick however was probably played on him but that, little by little and as dusk began to gather, he found himself interested almost to impatience, perplexed almost to pain. His companion on the wall indescribably *lived*, and yet lived only to cheat him. When he had at last in meditation fixed the ground of his complaint he found in it the quite defensible position that, painted as people are always painted, the subject would have had something to say to him. That was a contention valid enough, and one with which he was at last able to associate his grievance. He had somehow lost a friend by the perversity of the posture—he was so sure of the friend he should have gained had the face been presented.

The more he looked at everything else the less it was credible there should have been anything to hide. The subject had been young, gallant, generous; these things, even on the scant showing, were his mysteries and marks. Ralph ended in fact by asking himself what other mere male back would so have produced the effect of sharpening curiosity. It was enough to say for this gentleman's close compact dark curls, for his long straight neck, which emerged from a high stock and rolled collar, for the fall of his shoulder and the cut of his dark-green sleeve, from the way his handsome left hand, folding easily over a pair of grey gloves, rested its knuckles on his hip and conveyed the impression of a beaver, of the earliest years of the century, held out of view in the right—it was enough to say for these few indications that they provoked to irritation the desire for others. He was a son of his time, and his time was the dawn of the modern era—which, bringing him to that extent within range, made it more of an offence to curiosity so to have missed him. He was a young English gentleman of a happy "position" and of a time in which his youth, given that position, could only be dedicated to the god of all the battles of which Waterloo was to be the greatest and the last. Who could say what had become of him or on what far-off field of Spain or of Flanders he mightn't have left his life? These were rare questions and quick flights, though Ralph had in truth on his first visit begun to presume and combine and construct. With opportunities renewed he had arrived under the effect of the last occasion previous at a complete and consistent scheme of vision. These present hours disconcerted him therefore the more that they poured again the elements into the crucible. The violet fumes went up afresh, but were thick and confounding. It was not that he didn't, the figure in the frame, remain extraordinarily persuasive, but that he on the contrary quite harassed credulity. It was not that there was less of him than one wanted, but rather that there was too inordinately much and that there would be more and more of the measure to come. Ralph repeatedly felt, as he let himself go, that it would come in force. He was like the worshipper in a Spanish church who watches for the tear on the cheek or the blood-drop from the wound of some wonder-working effigy of Mother or of Son. When he moved away a little it was to let these things start at their ease, and when he next turned upon them it was to assist at the prodigy before it should stop.

It must at the same time be mentioned that he knew at moments the chill of intermissions, that he had more than once to shake himself in the lapse of faith. He saw during these revulsions but what he had seen before, the sharpest mere suggestion, no doubt, in the whole range of the effective art of suggestion. The young man looked away, but not from any embarrassment that he could produce. It wasn't what he hid that he thought of, but what he saw for himself. The practical snub to poor Ralph was thus that he looked away into a world of his own—off into the dark backward that at once so challenged and so escaped his successor. Just so his own was in his tremendous "pull" and reach, the fact of his positively living enjoyment of some relation or other, not to say some cluster of relations, that during those very minutes determined his considering air, and even, of a sudden, invested him with something of that effect which poor Ralph, wondering about great Italian church pictures and ruefully conscious of knowing them but by hearsay, imputed to the beauty and sincerity of the portrayed, the attentive donatorio in the corner of the Venetian or other masterpiece. What was the presence of the pious magnifico, say, but our very Ralph Pendrel's presence, not a little mixed, as he supposed that of the old-time devotee represented in the act to be, with the immemorial smoke of altar candles?—yet leaving the upper spaces, those where the sacred or the saintly image itself reigned, clear and sublime. The clearness, or call it even the sublimity, was here for all the world the same sort of thing: didn't it place round the handsome uplifted head, as by the patina of the years, the soft rub of the finger of time, that ring of mystic light? In the Titian, the Tintoret or the Veronese such a melting of the tone, such a magic as grew and grew for Ralph as soon as he once had caught the fancy of it, would have expressed the supernatural even as the circling nimbus expresses.

He had at intervals an eye to his watch, but what kept him on and on was precisely the force of the stillness in which nothing happened. There had come to him at the end of an hour or two a special and peculiar sense of being alone in the house. If his good friends in charge were below—he had had with them this evening no contact—never were good friends so respectful of what he was quite ready to call for their sake his absurdity. He was fully aware of how absurd it might appear in a quiet gentleman of unannounced intentions to perambulate an ordered house after the fashion of some carpet-man or plumber deprived by a catastrophe of foot-rule or pocket-book. He listened at the mouth of the lower regions and found them soundless; he remounted to the chambers above, and then he again descended to apply that test. Practically, in any case, he was beyond all observation and if self-effaced agents but worked to make him feel so, that only assured the freedom. Perhaps they had in fact gone out, finding him in murmured counsel more uncanny than they liked; it came to him whimsically while he paused anew at one of the windows as if on purpose to feel cut off by the gathering night and the patter of cold rain, it came to him agreeably that they might have been scared of a person whose range was so restless, who, declining at the outset a fire, seemed to like the gruesome chill, and who now let the shadows multiply without so much as ringing for a light.

The windy lanterns flickered in the square and were reflected in the wet, and as he turned about for another prowl—his last decidedly this one—he assured himself that he had in his pocket matches for tobacco and that, should he require them, the numerous brave stiff candle-sticks of silver and brass (oh what people he knew, even Aurora herself, would have given for them!) were furnished with tall tapers. On his reaching again for his final round the first drawing-room, which occupied with its fine windows the width of the house and into which, as the curtains were still undrawn, the street-lamp before the outer door played up with a gusty rise and fall that made objects, chairs, cabinets, sofas, pictures, look the least bit equivocal and like some vague human company that blinked or grimaced at him—on his thus finding himself once more where he seemed most to hold the key of the place he resumed the pointless pacing that had occupied so much of his visit. He walked from end to end as with a problem to think out; listened to his tread on the carpetless floor, for the perfect polish of which (no material note in the whole scale being more to his taste) he had made from the first a point of commending the housekeeper; he stayed on without knowing why, only clinging to this particular room just because he could measure its length, and even a little because of the very ambiguity, half sociable and half sinister, that made its different features, as he might have said, take action. He trifled at moments with the idea of spending the night—which he was indeed spending to the extent that he so hung on. Nights spent in peculiar houses were a favourite theme of the magazines, and he remembered tales about them that had been thought clever—only regretting now that he had not heard on the retreat of his fellow-occupants (for was not that always the indispensable stroke?) the terrified bang of the door. The real deterrent to sitting up at Number Nine would just be, he lucidly reasoned, its coincidence with the magazines. Nothing would induce him, he could at least fondly convince himself, to make the place the subject of one of the vulgar experiments that pass into current chatter. He would presently go with his mind made up; but meanwhile he walked.

He walked and walked—walked till he received a check in the form of a bump from a piece of furniture. This brought him back to the fact of the complete fall of night and to more darkness in the room than his enlarged vision had for the time needed to reckon with. He looked about him and felt as cold as if he had really passed a vigil; without his certainty that he had been on his legs he might fairly believe he had slept. He wondered what time had elapsed, but, taking out his watch to see, found its face indistinct even at the window. He then felt in his waistcoat for matches, but immediately after, in the act of striking one, had a happy change of thought. It was as if he had already proof positive of being there alone. It was vivid to him at this instant, in the flame of his match, that for reasons he didn't stop to question—the fact itself made so for intenser moments—he had been peculiarly disconnected and *left*, left to himself and to whatever else might be; with which consciousness he instead of consulting his watch, though he took another look about, made for the first candlestick that just showed its upright silver gleam. His match went out before he reached it, but he struck another, and it was in the act of lighting the candle that his hand told him how he trembled. This was the shake, he felt, however, of excitement—not of a baser state of nerves; an excitement that marked simply his at last knowing himself, as not yet, in possession of what he had come in for. His doubt was settled: he had asked himself if he were prepared, if he should "elect," to be; but here he was, in fine, without more question or more ado. The only ado was, with his candle lighted, to face the consequence of that particular preparation.

This act employed him, thanks to the bunchy wick, a minute or two; but no sooner was the little flame assured and he had raised aloft the glimmering torch than he was filled with the sense of a quite new relation to the house. It was but a trifle, yet he had not hitherto so much used the place even as to light a candle. This triviality made all the difference of raising him from the condition, comparatively poor, of a visitor who betrayed timidity. It registered in a single brief insistence the fact that he was master, and when he now almost waved in the air his light, of which the wax hadn't time to melt, it was in sign—tremble though his hand still might—of a confidence sharply gained. The impression was strong with him of having traversed a crisis—served, and all in half an hour, one of those concentrated terms of pious self-dedication or whatever by which the aspirants of the ages of faith used to earn their knighthood. What was it he had emerged from after this fashion of the accepted probationer? He had had his idea of testing the house, and lo it was the house that by a turn of the tables had tested him. He had at all events grasped his candle as if it had been sword or cross, and his attitude may pass for us as sufficiently his answer or his vow. It had already occurred to him that, so completely consecrated, he must make one more round. He moved to the end of the room and then moved back; it had begun to give him extraordinary pleasure thus to march with his light. He marched out to the lobby and the staircase and then down, slow and solemn, to the hall he had supposed Jacobean and in which, illumined, he could once more, by the mere play of his arm, make due amends for his mistake. He came up again to the landing by the great room and, after a slight hesitation, continued his ascent. He revolved through the chambers above and amused himself, at successive windows, with the thought of the observation possibly incurred, out in the square, by such a wandering twinkle from floor to floor and in the small hours on the part of some soaked and sleepy policeman not already, in respect to the old house, without a working hypothesis. On his return to the level of the drawing rooms he had another of his pauses; he stood with his candle aloft and his eyes attached a minute to the door that, open at the end of the passage, would have admitted him straight to the panelled parlour.

The effect of this consideration was that he went roundabout, turning directly again to the front and the row of dark windows lashed afresh by a great gust of the rain. It was as if the wind had of a sudden grown wild in order to emphasise with its violence all the elements of his case. It was somehow too by this time—with such a stride—two o'clock in the morning and terrible weather. The forward exposure most met the assault, the small square black panes rattled in their tall white sashes, the objects around him creaked, and his candle came as near going out as if a window had blown through. The commotion was in fact so great, shaking all the place, that under the sense of the draught he wasn't for the moment sure something hadn't somewhere been forced open. He instinctively moved, half for inquiry, half for shelter, to the inner room, the second; which brought him, still with his clutched and raised light, to view of the other door of the panelled parlour, the access independent of the hall. He had after this an instant of confusion, an instant during which he struck himself as catching at a distance the chance reflection of his candle-flame on some polished surface. If the flame was there, however, where was the surface?—the duplication of his light showing, he quickly perceived, in the doorway itself. He received in those instants an amazing impression—knew himself convinced that in his absence the thing he had thought of and put away had taken place. Somebody was in the room more prodigiously still than he had dreamed—on his level, on the floor itself and but ten yards off, and now, all intelligence and response, vividly aware of him, fixed him across the space with eyes of life. It was like the miracle prayed for in the church—the figure in the picture had turned; but from the moment it had done so this tremendous action, this descent, this advance, an advance, and as for recognition, upon his solitary self, had almost the effect at first of crushing recognition, in other words of crushing presumption, by their immeasurable weight. The huge strangeness, that of a gentleman there, a gentleman from head to foot, to meet him and share his disconnection, stopped everything; yet it was in nothing stranger than in the association that they already, they unmistakeably felt they had enjoyed. With this last apprehension at any rate the full prodigy was there, for what he most sharply knew while he turned colder still was that what he had taken for a reflection of his light was only another candle. He knew, though out of his eye's range any assurance, that the second of the pair on the shelf below the portrait was now not in its place. He raised his own still higher to be sure, and the young man in the doorway made a movement that answered; but so, while almost as with brandished weapons they faced each other, he saw what was indeed beyond sense. He was staring at the answer to the riddle that had been his obsession, but this answer was a wonder of wonders. The young man above the mantel, the young man brown-haired, pale, erect, with the high-collared dark blue coat, the young man revealed, responsible, conscious, quite shining out of the darkness, presented him the face he had prayed to reward his vigil; but the face—miracle of miracles, yes—confounded him as his own.

BOOK THIRD

The upshot of the state in which he found himself for three or four days was a sudden decision to call on the Ambassador. The idea, in coming to him, brought him ease, offered an issue to his pressing need to communicate. He had been divided between this need and the equal one—the profound policy—of silence; than which conflict nothing in his life had ever more tormented him. He wished he had been a Catholic, that he might go to confession; his desire, remarkably enough, being no less for secrecy than for relief. He recalled the chapter in Hawthorne's fine novel in which the young woman from New England kneels, for the lightening of her woe, to the old priest at St. Peter's, and felt that he sounded as never before the depth of that passage. *His* case in truth was worse than Hilda›s and his burden much greater, for she had been but a spectator of what weighed upon her, whereas he had been a close participant. It mattered little enough that his sense was not the sense of crime; it was the sense, in an extraordinary degree, of something done in passion, and of an experience far stranger than a mere glimpse, or than, if it came to that, a positive perpetration, of murder. He wondered that a knowledge of anything less than murder could be able to constitute in one's soul such a closed back room; but what was of course now most present to him was that he had hitherto grasped of life a sadly insignificant shred. There were at least as many more things in it for one's philosophy than poor Hamlet himself was to have found in heaven and earth. He went about and took his food and did his business; he had tested the truth of the promise made, the promise that he should successively present, even to himself, on reappearance; he was in fact fully aware that he had never yet *had* for the world—yes, and perhaps too for himself—so much to rest on as in the appearance he presented.

Nothing perhaps was more strange than that what he had accepted he still accepted; he was not attended with disorders or fears; he had neither alarms nor lapses nor returns, neither cold sweats nor hot flushes: it was much nearer true that he found in the excitement—for it was after all, however muffled and compressed, the felt throb of a pulse—an inordinate charm. But if it might be a charm, for the time, as much as one would, just so it might become later on, and was probably sure to, a terror; whatever form one should finally best know it by, he wanted in some single instance to impart his knowledge. He desired, he chose, that one other person, anxiously selected, should share his charge of it. One person would do—in fact more than one would spoil everything. There was a difference for him that he conceived this would make if he could only be sure of the safety of the vessel. His word once dropped into that moral receptacle and the key turned upon it and pocketed, he should come the more assuredly back to life, or might rather, and as for the first time, attack and perhaps surmount it. The motive he obeyed was indeed on the occasion of the visit itself as completely expressed as might be. The Ambassador, blest and distinguished man, was not a personal friend, was only the friend of friends. These latter had so taken the field that Ralph was more "introduced" than he had ever been to anyone, or than his Excellency could ever have known any bearer of letters. Such, however, was the high urbanity of this personage that our young man was as well received as if the heralds had been dumb. To the blare of trumpets Ralph had moreover not himself contributed, leaving his letters at the Embassy as little as elsewhere: he only knew that suggestion would have been applied from over the sea without action of his own, and this in fact put further delay at odds with good manners. It was sufficient that the representative of his country should be pre-eminent, accomplished, witty and kind, and that, much addicted to good cigars, he should usually be accessible at about six o'clock.

On the spot of course and in presence of his easy host, who must have adopted, he could see, defensively and professionally, the plan of taking for granted only the usual—it was naturally there and so difficult enough to state; at the same time that he had not been three minutes in the room without feeling how fully he should at last deliver himself. The way, it was true, was not smoothed by the Ambassador's remark that he knew all about him: there was at present so much more to know than even an Ambassador could possibly imagine. He remembered his excellent father; and was also good enough to mention that he remembered his beautiful mother, concerning whose later years he inquired; and they talked for some minutes of the several friends who had, as his Excellency was so good as to call it, brought them together, and of whom our young man found himself surprised, for particular reasons, to be able to give coherent news. He felt the charm of his host's tone, with its note of free recognition, which seemed to make him for the moment something almost of an equal; and yet even while he wondered if these were perhaps not, as minor instances, high refinements of that very diplomacy which he had studied, afar off, in dusty books and tracked through the wilderness of history, he was quite aware of not being made ashamed, as a person received with such special marks possibly ought to have been, of what he had there up his sleeve. He was only a little abashed when the Ambassador, who had read everything, spoke of having read his book and found it remarkably clever. He himself had learnt three days after landing in England how clever it wasn't, but the case was now above all that this faint effort of a groundless presumption had forfeited even such claim to existence as might belong to some nameless baby of the prehistoric age who should have died at birth. But only after he had shaken his head quite sadly and too sharply had he the sense of having, by this contradiction, appeared to attribute to his entertainer more innocence than was altogether just. He had not at all events come to put him in his place, and his need was immediately, that this should be clear, to explain for what he *had* come—a question the more urgent as he was really full of it to the brim. "I know but too well," he said, "that nine compatriots out of ten approach you with a Story. But no strayed maniac of them all can have bored you with one like mine."

The Ambassador, from his deep chair, in his "own" room on the ground floor, where books and papers were many and colours brown and sounds soft, smiled across the old Turkey rug through his beard and his fumes. "Is it very, very good?"

"For credibility no. But for everything else," said poor Ralph, "lovely."

"And very, very long?"

"Only as long—beyond the prime fact or two—as your Excellency himself may make it. It hasn't for me somehow at all that sort of dimension. I don't *know* at least how long it is. I wish I did!»

"Do you mean," the Ambassador asked, "that it's only broad? Why don't you, with your cleverness," he pursued before his visitor could answer, "put it on paper?"

"They generally do write them, you mean?" Ralph on his side returned. "I daresay, but if I did, you see, you might be obliged by the rules of your position to reply—not that I'm at all acquainted with them; and any reply is exactly what I ask your leave to assure you that my communication absolutely doesn't look for. I simply want to make it—so that I shan't be the only person living to know; and my sole request of you is kindly to keep it altogether to yourself.

There's nothing in the world you can 'do.' You can't lend me money. I've the advantage, which I fully appreciate, of having enough for my business. I'm not in love—or at least if I am it's not what I propose to trouble you with. I'm not in a scrape—that is I hope I'm not; for if I shall prove to be I fear the good offices of the Embassy even will scarce avail me and that I shall have to get out of it very much as I've got in."

"And how *have* you got in?" the Ambassador went on.

Ralph already felt how right his idea had been and how this application of it would help him. It was as if he had held in his hand the key he wished to confide for safe keeping. His friend's face—by this time quite that of a friend—was by itself as perfect a promise as the case required. It was exactly as if the key—too precious an object to be carried about the person—were to be taken over before his eyes and placed in the official strong-box. "I think, sir, you *will* make it long."

"That won't matter if I don't find it so."

His Excellency had spoken with such kindness that Ralph laughed out. It was the kindness of indulgence; he saw, as he thought, what was behind it. "I'm at the worst," he replied, "one of the quiet kind—for I'm sure you see all sorts; but I shall nevertheless, if you'll pardon me, need to move a little as I talk." He was in fact out of his chair, and as he remained there before the fire, on the rug, the men exchanged a long look, a look which, as it gave the younger everything he wanted, must also more or less have comprised some gain for the elder. Ralph was willing to be taken for anything: he didn't mind the estimate—all that was important was the considerate form. It had quite begun, as we have seen, to draw him on and on. "I shan't even expect you to believe me," he after an instant resumed, "I simply say to myself that my secret is one that your own interest will lead you to keep—though it can be but an interest merely intellectual, not at all official; if you permit me," our young man finally smiled, "to make the difference. I somehow see that you'll be sure to feel that giving it any publicity would somehow spoil it for you."

The Ambassador blandly smoked. "You mean I must keep it for my pleasure?"

Ralph, who had declined with thanks so much as a cigarette, met this from where he had continued to stand. "That will be exactly my strength. It will leave me as much at ease as the seal of confession. And there's another thing," he frankly added, "I don't fear to appear ridiculous; but with your Excellency, naturally, it won't be the same."

His Excellency was too delightful. "You don't fear to appear ridiculous to *me.* That›s all. I can meet you at least on the same ground. I shan›t fear to appear so to you. I›m perfectly willing," he went on, "to give you my definite word. If you do tell nobody else you may take it that I shall tell as little."

Ralph watched him a moment. "You think I *will* tell somebody else?»

The Ambassador got up at this to help himself from the chimney-piece to another cigar, the end of which he nipped off and lighted before replying. When he did reply it was with a reassuring hand on Ralph's shoulder. "No—it's just what I *don't* think. Your difficulty in expressing it, whatever it may be, strikes me as the gage of your general reserve."

The words were as kind as all the others, but they practically, and happily enough, acted for Ralph as a challenge. He took it up then, and it afterwards appeared that, in the act, he had also taken the Ambassador's left hand, removing it by his own right from his shoulder, where it had remained in soothing and, as he was sure, rather compassionate intent. He thus appropriated the protection which enabled him after an instant: "The point is that I'm not myself."

But his friend smiled as if in tribute to his lucidity. "Oh yes you are!"

Ralph's look, on this, seemed to deprecate, and even in still greater pity, any tendency to the superficial; it being marked for him more and more that what had happened to him made him see things in a way compared to which the ways of others—positively of such brilliant others as his host—could show but for the simplest. "You don't take it as I mean it; or rather perhaps I should say I don't mean it as you take it. Take it, however," he pursued, "as you must: I have the advantage that your courtesy to me leaves both of us such a margin." And then he explained. "I'm somebody else."

The Ambassador's hand had during these instants still submitted to his own for reassurance; but its possessor now disengaged it and turned away, briefly presenting a meditative back. He was soon reestablished none the less in his chair with his fresh cigar and every preparation, it would seem, for the issue. Yet he smoked another moment. "And is the other person you?"

"That's what I count him; though for certainty one should be able to ask him—which one isn't. It's he himself only who can know; and I've enough," said Ralph, "with my own side of the matter. But the whole affair," he continued, "was that we should exchange identities; an arrangement all the more easy that he bears an extraordinary resemblance to me and that on my first meeting him I even made the mistake of taking him for a wondrous reflection—in a glass or wherever—of my own shape."

The Ambassador was slow; yet as Ralph, once launched, panted a little, he had the effect of breaking in. "And did he take you for a reflection of his? You're sure," he asked, "that you know which of you is which?"

Ralph waited a little; then very gently and reasonably, "Be as patient as you can with me," he returned. "You shall have it all, and as clear as possible. But be very kind." His host, as to correct the idea of anything else, made a quick expressive movement, which was, however, checked by our friend's manner. "It's a most extraordinary thing, you see, to have befallen a man, and I don't wonder at the queer figure I must make to you. But you'll see too for yourself in a moment how easily you'll wish to let me down. It's the most extraordinary thing that ever happened in the world—but at the same time there's no danger," he cheerfully declared, "of my losing my way. I'm all here, or rather"—Ralph was gay about it—"*he* is.»

There was little enough doubt of how his confidant would let him down; and, the idea of his being "humoured" apart, he welcomed whatever would help him. There was at any rate no failure of respect in the next attentive inquiry. "But who is this party to your remarkable affair? Or if you would rather I should put it so, who was he? I mean," said the Ambassador, "before what you call your exchange."

"Just exactly, by the amazing chance, what I was myself—and what I am still, for that matter; the strangest part of all being that it doesn't interfere nearly as much as you might suppose, and that I'm in fact not nearly so different."

The way the Ambassador followed amounted—though it wasn't so wonderful in him—to inspiration. "So different as I might suppose from what you were before?"

Ralph's face became a tribute to such prompt intelligence. "I'm still a gentleman, thank God; and no bigger fool, either, than I already was. I'm not worse looking, even if I'm not better."

"You couldn't very well be better!" his companion handsomely replied.

But Ralph was now so full of the whole fact itself as scarce to appreciate the compliment. "If I'm so very much the same thing I'm still an American, you see—and not a Briton."

"I'm awfully glad of that!" the Ambassador laughed.

"Oh it's the great point—our common ground. I mean mine and his. We're both here—at the same age—for the first time, and but freshly disembarked. That is," said our young man, "we *were.*" It pulled him up a little, but not, he was instantly eager to show, too much. "I'm not losing my way—it comes to the same thing."

But he had had to consider it, and the Ambassador smoked. "If that then is the case with everything, what is—or what was the difference?"

"Between us?"—Ralph was prompt. "Nothing but our age."

"But I thought you said your age was the same."

"Oh," Ralph explained, "I meant in the sense of our time, our period. That's the difference of the greater part of a century. It was then—that time ago—he came over."

There would have been a failure of verisimilitude if his host hadn't visibly wondered. "And where has he been since?"

Ralph looked an instant, from where he stood, through the window and out into the world of things less strange than those he might so well be felt to have filled the room with. But if he was grave he was not blank. "You see I don't know everything." And for a moment again he dropped.

During this lapse the Ambassador on his side smoked; to the effect of his presently saying: "Is he ninety—nine years old?"

It brought back his visitor. "No—for if he were I should be; and I'm exactly thirty, which does very well; for since I've become him, in particular, I call it young." Ralph hung fire—but really from the sense of now so interesting his auditor that keeping it up was almost a strain. Quite for himself, however, nothing was easier. "He's magnificent. He's really beautiful." That indeed made him catch himself, and this time he turned away. "What I mean is he *was!* Before he ceased to be?»

"He hadn't—or he hasn't," Ralph returned, "ceased to be; for if that were the case I myself shouldn't be here before you in the solid soundness I've undertaken to impress you with. He was in a perfect prime that it was a joy, as a fellow-countryman, to behold. It was in that form that he again, for an hour, existed to me."

"For an hour?" the Ambassador asked as if to be exact.

"It was probably less—even for all that passed between us; but the fact of my situation is that he did exist."

"Is the fact of your situation that you've seen a ghost?"

"Oh," Ralph raised his head high to say, "I decline to admit for a moment that he was *that.* He was much better than any ghost.»

It seemed to make for the Ambassador a distinction that he desired to grasp. "'Better'?"

"Well, much more contrary to nature."

"I don't understand then," the Ambassador said, "why you don't rather call it worse. Isn't the impression strange in proportion as it's contrary to nature, and isn't it by the same token agitating or upsetting or appalling, for any relation with such a matter, in proportion as it's strange?" After which he went on while Ralph felt his considering look: "Do you really *like* such impressions?»

"I see I'm an impression to you—and of course an extraordinary one; but he wasn't one to me," Ralph pursued, "in any such sense as that—for the interest of our relation, as you justly term it, is so much more interesting, you see, than any with which, even at the best, I can hope to inspire you. He was a man as substantial for me as I am—or as I *was!*" Ralph pulled up a moment to smile—"for myself; and interesting most of all, I suppose, because so extraordinarily interested."

"Interested in *you?*" his host inquired as with the care to avoid alike too much or too little gravity.

"Well, yes—interested in me by his being so possessed of the kind of thing that interests us both. I've been ridden all my life, I think I should tell you"—for our young man thought it but fair to develop this—"by the desire to cultivate some better sense of the past than has mostly seemed sufficient even for those people who have gone in most for cultivating it, and who with most complacency," Ralph permitted himself to add, "have put forth their results. So you can fancy what a charm it was," he wound up, "to catch a person, and a beautifully intelligent one, in the very act of cultivating——"

The Ambassador was on his feet at this, with an effect of interruption, as by the very quickness of his apprehension. "His sense of the present!" he triumphantly smiled.

But his visitor's smile reduced that felicity. "His sense of the future, don't you see?—which had at last declined to let him rest, just as my corresponding expression had declined to let me. Only after his being worried," Ralph's scruple explained, "nearly a century longer."

"A century's a long time to be worried!" the Ambassador remarked through his smoke, but permitting himself this time a confession of amusement.

"Oh a terrible time of course—but all leading up, you see, to this tremendous relief I've brought him. I've brought him, I've given him, I've introduced him to, the Future. So there we are!" Ralph gloried.

His companion, though visibly impressed, appeared a little to wonder where indeed they were. Then this wonder found voice. "How could you bring him what you didn't have yourself?"

Ralph needed but a moment to consider. "Why, I *am* the Future. The Future, that is, for *him*; which means the Present, don't you see——?"

"The Present, I see, for *me!*" his host, fairly flushed with divination, broke in.

"Yes," Ralph promptly returned, "nothing could do more beautifully than your Present, not to say, literally, your presence, for the Future he has waited so long, poor dear chap, to know about."

"What it comes to then," the Ambassador considered in all apparent sympathy—"what it comes to in fine," this functionary smoked, "is that I and my contemporaries *are* his Future.»

Ralph accepted the conclusion. "It would come to that if he could get into relation with you."

It might have been by reason of something conveyed in his visitor's tone that the Ambassador said: "With me in particular you mean?"

Ralph met it handsomely. "Ah I could wish nothing better for him than you!"

"And nothing better for me than him?"

Ralph kept his eyes kindly on his country's representative. "Yes, since I find you so remarkably good for myself."

The Ambassador acknowledged the tribute, yet couldn't but formulate after all a certain inward confusion. "I'm only puzzled by your not having spoken to me of your friend and yourself a moment ago as separate persons—but on the contrary of your having arrived, wasn't it? at some common identity or wonderful unity. You *are* the other fellow, you said, didn›t you?—and the other fellow, by the same stroke, is you. So that when I wonder where the other fellow is,» he genially pursued, "it would seem that I've only to suppose him here in this room with me, in your interesting person."

These words might have struck us as insidious enough just to trip up our young man, but his lucidity was in fact perfectly proof. "I didn't say, kindly understand, that we have *merged* personalities, but that we have definitely exchanged them—which is a different matter. Our duality is so far from diminished that it›s only the greater—by our formulation, each to the other, of the so marked difference in our interest. The man ridden by his curiosity about the Past *can't*, you'll grasp, be one and the same with the man ridden by his curiosity about the Future. He has given me his chance for this, while I have given him mine for that. Recognise accordingly," said Ralph, "that we're at the opposite poles—or at least in quite different places."

It was wonderful more and more what the Ambassador *could* recognise by the aid of his kind wise little intervals of thought and indulgences of contemplation. "Yes, yes—but if I of course see that you, as the distinct individual you are so fortunately able to claim to be, stand here delightfully before me, that doesn't in the least tell me where *he* is located, as we say, in time and space."

"Why, he's down at the door in the cab," Ralph returned with splendid simplicity.

His host might have been lost for a moment in the sheer radiance of it—even to the point indeed of a gesture guarding against excess of impression or for that matter just gaining time. "Do you mean to say you're all this while keeping your hansom?"

"It's not a hansom—in this eternal rain: it's a four-wheeler with the glasses up. And he only wants," our young man explained, "to wait as long as I require. So at least I understand," he remarked as an afterthought.

"So that you'll find him—in his rather tried patience, it strikes me—when you go down? And I should have the pleasure of seeing him too," the Ambassador further ventured, "if I were to go down with you?"

This truly was the first of his Excellency's questions to induce in our friend a pause at all ominous. "Surely—if he has *not*, under the strain of my absence, as you suggest, gone off on his own account."

The Ambassador faced this contingency. "Where in that case will he have gone?"

"Why, as I've explained, into the Future. Say," Ralph threw off, "into Regent Street or Piccadilly." And then as his companion, at this, frankly laughed out: "They didn't exist, you see, at that time in any such form as they have to-day."

"I see, I see"—his Excellency again was prepared. "But fancy them," he clearly couldn't help at the same time exclaiming, "fancy *them* the reward for him of so sublime a self-projection!»

"Well," Ralph readily reasoned, "my idea is that, with all they represent for him, they're not unlikely to prove as great a reward as any this extravagance of my own may come in for."

"It's wonderful for me," the Ambassador soon replied, "by which I mean it's quite out of my common routine, to allow myself—as you see I do!—such intimate strange participations. I understand you that I'm to regard myself as mixed in the concern of your friend down there no less than in your own."

Ralph considered of that, but with all equanimity and to the upshot of his saying very naturally: "You want to be sure, properly enough, of what you may at the worst be let in for; you want to be guaranteed against undue inconvenience. Well, I don't think I see you let in for anything worse than having thus heard me out and taken my name and address." With which our young man smiled. "May they lie light on your conscience!"

"They will lie there, I assure you, in a place quite of their own"—and the Ambassador took up the card brought in to him on his visitor's arrival and left close at hand. "This shall be carefully preserved, and I shall cherish, for the interest you inspire me with, the good hope of our some time meeting again."

Ralph didn't discourage this hope, though whatever support he offered it was but to be inferred from what was left for recognition of such connections in his more and more preoccupied face. That countenance, charged for a moment with further fair acknowledgments, seemed to turn away from them, before they were uttered, in the interest of something more urgent. "Of course I perfectly understand that you think me, that you must think me, more or less raving mad. I perfectly understand that you must want to keep me in view and be able as far as possible to track me and give some account of me in case of future inquiry. I appreciate that, and it was even exactly for it, I think, that I came. I really believe I ought to be tracked, to be subject to identification, to have an eye kept on me. I'm like one starting a perhaps perilous journey and wanting not to have neglected precautions in advance. I don't in the least mind your thinking me mad—I should be so, or should be at least idiotic, not to conceive my making the impression. At the same time I strike myself as of a sanity I've never enjoyed before. Don't be afraid of offending me, for what is it but your very protection against myself that I've thus invoked? Not that I fear I shall destroy myself—at least in any common way; I'm so far from intending or wishing to commit suicide that I'm proposing to push my affair all the way it will go, or in other words to live with an intensity unprecedented."

"Well, if you live with the intensity to which you help others I don't see what responsibility you're likely to be accused of shirking. *I* can›t keep still,» the Ambassador then flatly declared, "till I've been down with you to verify that question of your friend in the cab."

Ralph offered so little objection to this—his looking for a moment intensely grave about it amounting to no real objection—that they had within a couple of minutes more descended together to the hall; where the servant in waiting, Ralph was afterwards to reflect, must at once have attested his conviction that his master was not simply seeing to the door a visitor of no inscribed importance. His Excellency would therefore be going further—under some exceptional stress; and to this end would have been placed without delay in possession of his hat, gloves and stick; equipped with which objects it verily was that the Ambassador presently stood with his guest on the outer pavement and in presence of the waiting vehicle, any further domestic attendance repressed and the door of the house closed behind them. There they remained a little, it may be mentioned—long enough at least for the exchange of a smile now rather strained on either side, strained even to breaking, possibly, before Ralph could decide to approach his cab near enough for an effective view of its inner state. He had before this checked the motion of the roused driver, dozing on the box, toward a heavy officious descent, and then had himself faced the consequences of another step and a sufficient thrust of his head through the window of his "growler" to assure himself of the degree of dissimulation under which a conceivable companion might lurk there. His renewed look at the Ambassador after this was a confession that nothing lurked, though without its being at all a confession of consequent defeat; so that, himself opening the door and inviting his distinguished friend to pass in, he signalled a perfect readiness to explain disappointment away. The Ambassador, it must be added, allowed him at once and ever so considerately the largest license of apology for the production of a groundless hope; the great man's words in fact represented a glance at grounds that had lived their little hour.

"His failure of patience through my having kept you so long—you did, I recognise, mention the possibility of that," was his Excellency's noble remark.

There came to Ralph's assistance on this a suddenly enlarged interest of vision; he had indeed within the house given utterance to that precautionary thought, but it was for all the world as if the same idea on the lips of his friend suggested something to go on with beyond even what his own intelligence had found. That was it!—nothing in the least discredited the report he had been occupied in making. That other party to the drive ending at the Embassy door was, with the most conceivable congruity, and thanks to a passion of curiosity that nothing could longer bridle, off on his own irresistible adventure: one had asked too much of him, at the point reached by their relation, in expecting so to choke off his own criticism. The interview upstairs had drawn itself out, and what had he had to do meanwhile, poor dear creature, but count the minutes that would lead to the striking of his hour? That the hour would strike for each of them as soon as the wise step now achieved had been taken—this had been their assumption on settling together that afternoon, so much more for the accommodation, when all was said, Ralph could see now, of the victim of the sense of the Past than for that of the victim of the sense of the Future. The latter, it came to our friend, taking no precaution and making no provision, none at least that one could one's self know anything about, brought the business a more hurrying passion: as would be perhaps of the very essence for a man so concerned as compared with a man concerned as he himself was. He was conscious of ten rather bedimmed seconds during which he had positively to see the appeal he had obeyed as a thing in itself inferior to the motive under the force of which his late companion, no longer able merely to oblige him, had doubtless begun to beat fine wings and test brave lungs in the fresh air of his experiment. He had the real start, so to speak, while the subject of the Ambassador's interest had doubtless only the advantage that might, on some contingency as yet of the vaguest, reside in that.

There thus breathed on our young man a momentary chill—which, however, didn't prevent the Ambassador's seating himself without further delay, nor his own perhaps slightly more contracted occupation of the second seat, nor their presently effective, their in fact rather confessedly contemplative, start for Mansfield Square. It was to appear to Ralph later on, at any rate, that they had at this stage been reduced to unembarrassed contemplation; which is perhaps indeed but a proof that while he gazed out of the cab window during this extraordinary progress what he looked at so fixedly as to take note of no interval of speech was neither the exhibition of successive streets, with their aspects and their varieties of identity, but the portentous truth of his being launched, since, so conclusively, his counterpart in the circumstance was, and of his fate's having thereby shut down on any backward step. Not that he wanted to take one, not that he wanted to take one——he kept repeating that as the vehicle rolled; to be as "in" for whatever awaited him as he now felt, as he now absolutely knew, himself, was a strong simplification—with which wasn't it positively a blest one too? which question had not been answered in the negative, at any rate, even by the time they pulled up at the address he had given. This was what had taken place during their transit, he afterwards knew; the minutes had been so wholly given, in their course, to his inwardly sealing the charter of accommodation, as he would have called it, to whatever might now confront him that after he had got out, on the stoppage of the cab, he addressed to his companion a "Will you keep it on?" which left things taken for granted between them without a scrap of a loose end dangling. *He* at least suffered none such, though there might have been just the sign of a difference in his good friend's face while the latter stepped straight out by way of answer. "Oh my dear man, I'll walk," he seemed to be saying; "I don't in the least mind your knowing that you've given me the fidgets or that I shall extremely need to think you over: which indulgence the use of my legs will healthily stimulate."

Something of that sort Ralph was much later on, as I say, to recover the appearance of his having found words for; just as he was to piece together the presumption that, the cabman paid, magnificently paid, and getting again into motion, he and his protector—for hadn't they after all rather exquisitely agreed to leave it at this?—stood face to face a little, under the prolongation of a handclasp; followed then by the mutual release that left his Excellency standing there on the pavement with the graver face of the two, *he* at least little doubted. Our young man was after that aware of a position of such eminence on the upper doorstep as made him, his fine rat-tat-tat-ah of the knocker achieved, see the whole world, the waiting, the wondering, the shrunkenly staring representative of his country included, far, far, in fact at last quite abysmally below him. Whether these had been rapid or rather retarded stages he was really never to make out. Everything had come to him through an increasingly thick *other* medium; the medium to which the opening door of the house gave at once an extension that was like an extraordinarily strong odour inhaled—an inward and inward warm reach that his bewildered judge would literally have seen swallow him up; though perhaps with the supreme pause of the determined diver about to plunge just marked in him before the closing of the door again placed him on the right side and the whole world as he had known it on the wrong.

BOOK FOURTH

I

He was so far prepared as that, on the footman's saying, after he had asked who was at home, "I think Miss Midmore is, sir," he had not been unduly agitated; though the effect was of making him at the same time wonder if he oughtn't, more decently, to have had his approach heralded in the course of the morning by the bearer of a note. Such questions as these, from the arrival of his ship at Plymouth, had repeatedly come up for him, and he had not lacked leisure, since the evening before, when the west country mail had set him down in Piccadilly amid a great bustle of general recognition, to advise his cousins of his immediate intention to wait on them. The sense had grown within him during the last three days that mistakes of one sort and another would easily be open to a young man just alighted from New York; he had made several already between Devonshire and London, even if without paying for them in heavier coin than a handful of new observations. His observations multiplied at such a rate that fifty to the minute would have been a short account of them; but there was one in particular that had from the first kept repeating itself and that might certainty have done as much to point his address as some of the others had done to remind him of danger. The danger was flagrant and consisted of the number of things to be known and reckoned with in England as compared to the few that had so sufficiently served him at home. He but wanted to know, though he would rather have liked to learn secretly; which for that matter he *was* now, he conceived, catching a little the trick of—and this in spite of his wonted way, from far back, on receipt of a new impression or apprehension of a new fact, and under correction, in particular, of a wrong premise; which was to lose himself quite candidly and flagrantly in the world of meaning so conveyed. That disclosed quantity was apt fairly to make him stand still for wonder—whereby it might well have happened that whosoever took note of him would scarce have known whether to conclude most on his simplicity or on his wit. If it was strange to have had so to wait for familiar appearances—familiar, that is, all round him, seemingly, to everyone but himself—it was perhaps more remarkable yet not to succeed in concealing how much one was on the spot ready to make of them by the working of some inward machinery.

The great reassurance just mentioned at any rate, and which ministered still more to surprise than to confidence, came from his somehow making out that Ralph Pendrel enjoyed an advantage beyond any he missed; had a manner, a look or a tone, some natural brightness, some undesigned but conciliatory art, which perceptibly paved his way and which perhaps, should he incline to presume upon it, might really gain him favour. This inference he had had, and without gross vanity, time to make—though arriving doubtless for the moment at no finer conclusion on it than that his spirits were all the while, beneath however small a bent to swagger or bluster, undiscourageably high, and that youth and good proportions, a clear face, a free hand and a brave errand, all borne on that tide, were capable of casting a spell of a sort that he should find occasion either to measure or to press. It had been odd assuredly to come thus soon to a thought of spells—especially in the midst of a consciousness of blunders; but it possibly reinforced a little even this degree of presumption that the very blunders, which might have been all to his confusion save that various other persons had promptly and obligingly, as it were, taken them over, appeared grandly imputable to the same spring of freshness. He couldn't deny to himself his eagerness—extraordinarily strong and which people made way for, to the extent even of a large margin, as if they liked to see it and to wait for what it might further show. It was an eagerness certainly to enjoy, yet not at any one's cost, any one's in particular; and this might to those dealing with him have seemed rare, or in other words have seemed charming, the sticking out of an impulse not as a pike on a charge but after the fashion of a beggar's hat presented for the receipt of alms. That was the figure, that the case—the pennies had hour after hour veritably rained in; and what but a perfect rattle of them, by that token, accompanied him at the footman's heels upstairs to where it could only be that Molly Midmore awaited—though perhaps but just in a general way—his presenting himself as a suitor for her hand?

He had been touched in the hall and on the staircase as by the faint odd brush of a suggestion that what was before his eyes during certain seconds had already been before them and was playing upon his attention, was quite *seeking* to, even though in the lightest, softest tug at it, by the recall of a similar case or similar conditions. Just so when the door above was opened to him and he heard himself announced the first flush of his impression was that of stepping straight into some chapter of some other story—other than his own of that moment, since he was by the evidence of every felt pulse up to his eyes in a situation, which glimmered upon him in the light, the bright strong light, of an aspect recognised; before failing of that effect indeed under his next full rush of perception. Wasn't it a place known, the great square wainscotted room, like several perhaps in which he had seen a sort of life led at home, only fairer and finer than those; with handsome objects and four or five portraits rather largely interspaced, and a daylight freshness in possession, the air at once of an outer clearness, of an emptier world looking in, and of windows unembarrassed to match, multiplied panes, one would say, but withal a prim spare drapery? It wouldn't have been that the world was emptier than he had known it beyond the sea, but that the scene itself, as it appeared for the ten seconds that challenged memory and comparison, would have worn its other face with a difference, confessing somehow to thicker shadows and heavier presences, the submission to a longer assault. Such matter of record, even on the part of a young man of the highest sensibility, is at the best elusive enough, however, and Ralph's general awareness was at once swallowed up in the particular positive certainty that nobody in all his experience in the least answered to the young lady seated near one of the windows before a piece of fine tense canvas framed and mounted on slim wooden legs, through which she was in the act of drawing a long filament of silk with the finest arm in the world raised as high as her head. He himself so far answered to something in her own intelligence that at sight and sound of him she slowly got up from before her work, with never a hint of interruption or confusion, and smiled across at him as if knowing all about him. She kept in this movement her arm still aloft—she might have been just balancing herself or wishing not to loosen her stitch; he was to remember afterwards how the crook of her little finger, in the raised hand, caught his eye at the distance, and how this helped him in a manner at once to take in that the arm itself, its sleeve shortened to very near the shoulder, was of the most beautiful rounded shape. That light of her knowing all about him doubtless helped to flood his own mind with the assurance immediately needed: he felt at this stage, in the most wonderful way, that things came to him, everything a right carriage required for the closer personal relation, in the very nick of being wanted, and wore thus, even under the gasp of a slight danger escaped, a certain charm and cheer of suddenness. That he was to make love, by every propriety, to Molly Midmore, and that he had in fact reached his goal on the very wings of that intention, this foretaste as of something rare had for days and days past hung about him like the scent of a flower persisting in life; but the sweetness of his going straight up to her with an offered embrace hadn't really been disclosed till her recognition, as we have said, breathed upon it with force and filled him at once with an extraordinary wealth of confidence.

He had stepped straight into that with his stepping into the room, and while he stood but long enough to know himself lifted and carried the taking in of what she was through all his senses completed the splendid rightness. Nothing might have been stranger than so repeated a jump, so flying a leap, to firm ground which hadn't been there before in any measurable manner but which his feet just felt beneath them at the crisis of need. Was it going to be enough simply to do the thing, whatever it might be, for it to "come" right, as they said, and for him above all to like it, as who should also say, after the fact? Surprising perhaps that questions of so comparatively general a kind should press with their air of particular business into an active apprehension unconditioned and absolute enough to forestall any conceivable lapse; yet nothing could well be pleasanter than such a quickening, and this even under the possibility that he might after a little get used to it. The young woman there in her capacious corner was admirably, radiantly handsome, and all the while still kept the posture she had at once risen to—kept it as for fear of his loss of the pleasure by her breaking it ever so little. The case was of course really that a mere moment sufficed for these enormities of attestation; the air roundabout them was prodigiously clean and clear, and so favoured happy certitude that by the time he had advanced a trifle further he was, in addition to everything else we have indicated, aware that, modest as she would indubitably prove, she was neither awkward nor shy, and was in fact quite as inspired and inflamed as himself. She came out from behind her frame, to which she had given a light push, and then it was that her splendid fairness, a complexion white and pink, and that her friendly laughing eyes and full parted lips and thickness of loose brown hair, helped the dress of sprigged muslin which kept as clear of her neck as it did of her elbows to tell him about her, from head to foot—and she was more than middling tall—everything that most pressingly concerned him. There played round him before he took her to his arms the glimmer of a comment kindled at some other flame than that of desire, the wonder of her being rather more imaged for him, and ever so typically, than likely to be, whatever fulness of reality awaited them, possessed by him; which pair of contradictions, however, melted together in the tide of happy intelligence that next flooded and seemed verily almost to drown them. That he should thus on the instant have clasped to his heart and his lips a young woman with whom in all his life he had never yet exchanged a word settled the relation for each alike as soon as it had been so nobly and freely sketched; which was again a case of that felt security after the fact already noted by him, as we have seen, and scarce open, of a truth, to more vivid illustration. The security was felt just as much by herself: this made the harmony full, this acted to keep it still quite possible for him that the comparatively superficial commerce, the inquiry and explanation that might have figured as preliminary, should follow at a lower level what had just taken place, and do so without either casting absurdity back on the passage or their themselves incurring ridicule.

"I reached London but last night—so you see I haven't lost much time. Perhaps I should first have asked your mother's leave," Ralph said; but she had already at the word taken him up.

"Oh she would certainly have given it!" And he at once saw from the tone of this that what she referred to as so licensed was the plunge into intimacy just enacted. It put him a trifle out of tune that the most he himself had meant was that he might have inquired of his cousin's convenience as to presenting himself; and to feel his deference to that propriety—or to almost any, it might seem—so swept away reminded him afresh that he couldn't, by every appearance, be too bold, since he plainly created in others, straight off and by his presence, the liveliest dispositions and allowances. If it was true that Mrs. Midmore, as he had figured her, would have smiled upon his silent rush at her daughter from their very threshold, what could this signify but that the house and the whole circle contained a treasure of welcome on which he was infinitely to draw? Well, it was still then in the highest degree agreeable to find everyone so understanding him as to help him to understand himself; no example of which felicity could be greater than such a promise of ease with the lady of Drydown, given the forms of deference he had tried to prepare himself to pay her. "You mustn't speak as if we have been thinking of you in the least as a stranger; for how can that be," Molly asked, "when everything was so made up between us all by your father's writing in that way to mamma so shortly before he died, wasn't it?" Her fine expressive eyes, he at once recognised, were charged with an appeal to him on the ground of this interesting history; and once more, after the merest repeated brush of the wing of that bewilderment by which he was thus effectually admonished and aided to escape, he knew the flood of consciousness within him to raise its level. His father, dear man, had died, his father had written, and even while they looked at each other under allusions so abounding it came and came and came that there had been an estrangement among those of their name on the two sides of the sea, and then, through a fortunate chance, a great healing of the breach, a renewal of good relations as to which his character of acclaimed wooer left no doubt. He was in actual free use of the whole succession of events, and only wanted these pages, page after page, turned for him: much as if he had been seated at the harpsichord and following out a score while the girl beside him stirred the air to his very cheek as she guided him leaf by leaf. She seemed verily after that fashion to hold out to his eyes the solemn scroll of history, on which they rested an instant to such a further effect of danger dissipated that before either she or he knew it they were once more in each other's arms. It was as if this repetition, this prolongation had been potently determined, and for each alike, by her free knowledge of what had gone before—he lagging a little behind, it was true, in the rapid review of reasons, but suddenly confident and quite abreast of her after they had thus irrepressibly and for the second time exchanged their vows. He had for the next thing even the sense of being, and in the gallantest way, beforehand with her when he heard himself strike out as from the push of multiplied forces behind him: there was all the notoriety—for what had it been *but* notoriety?—of the loyalism of the American Pendrels during the Revolution, in the rigour of which they had emigrated, restoring themselves to England for a ten years' stay and not a little indebted under that stress to the countenance and even the charity of their English kindred. A freshness of interest in this adventure surged through our young man's blood and sought expression, without the least difficulty, in an attitude about it to his young hostess as competent as if he had by some extraordinary turn become able to inform her ignorance.

"My grandfather—yes," he said, "must of course, thirty years ago have been rather a wild sort of character and anything but a credit to us. But he was terribly handsome, you know," Ralph smiled, "and if your great-aunt, while we hung on here, had cause to complain of his fickleness, I think we're all now aware that she fell quite madly in love with him and paid him attentions of an extravagance that he couldn't after all ignore—not in common civility." He liked to go back to that—since it was all indeed, under growing freedom of reference, so much more behind him than before; it was truly brave matter for talk, warming his blood, as we say, while it flowed; and he had at the end of another minute so mastered it that he would have liked to catch her mistaken in order to put her right. Her face, for that matter, glowed with the pleasure, wasn't it? of his assurance thus made positive; assurances, roundabout them, couldn't, she showed, too much multiply, and it wasn't to be till considerably after that the sense of this moment marked her for him as really rather listening, though in all delight, to his recital of a learnt lesson, than as herself taking from him an inspiration she might have lacked. He was amused—even if why so amused?—at the vividness of the image of the too susceptible or too adventurous daughter of their earlier house with whose affections, the acknowledged kinship of the two families offering approved occasion, his unscrupulous ancestor had atrociously trifled. The story had anything but grace, thanks to the facts of its hero's situation, his responsibility to a patient young wife and three children—these kept indeed at a distance, quartered, by his care, in a small French town, during most of the term of his extravagance; the climax of which last had been the brutal indifference, as it at least appeared, of his return to New York with nothing done for mitigation of the exposure awaiting the partner, as the phrase was, of his guilt. It didn't make the scandal less—since a different face might somehow or other have been put upon it—that he prospered in America against every presumption attaching to the compromised civil state of the family; that he succeeded in carrying their name again almost insolently high, in recovering and enlarging their ancient credit, in retrieving their wasted, their forfeited resources, in putting them at last back into such a posture that after his death and with the lapse of the condoning years they could perfectly pass for people, had in fact conspicuously become people, incapable not only of gross infractions but of the least lapse from good manners. The defunct worthy, with whatever discomfort of conscience, had had a high hand for affairs of profit and had flourished as the undoer of virtue or confidence or whatever other shaky equilibrium is often observed to flourish. The proofs of his mastery were naturally, however, much more evident to the followers in his line than any ground for imputations less flattering; with which it seemed further unmistakeable that a posterity in such good humour with itself and its traditions might have even enough of that grace to spare for cases of the minor felicity. How at any rate had it come about that the minor felicity, of all things in the world, could be a distinguishable mark of the English Pendrels, the legend of any awkward accident or any foregone advantage in whose annals would so scantly have emerged as matter for free reference? This was a question that might with the extraordinary swell of our young man's present vision find itself as answerable as the next before or the next after. Every question became answerable, in its turn, the moment it was touched; so that when his companion, as she had so bravely become, mentioned the repair of the family breach he jumped at the occasion for a full illustration of the subject.

"You see how little difference your mother's marriage made to us, with the extinction of our name here involved in it; since if Pendrels had at last failed us, for the pleasure over there of thinking of them, we could make Midmores answer almost as well at the worst—take *them* up even with a resignation which, now that I know you, cousin,» Ralph went on, «seems to put our acquaintance in a light that couldn›t possibly be bettered.»

"Certainly the Midmores are as good as anybody," the young lady bearing their name flared out in the charmingest way to reply; "for we're not forgetting, are we? that it was a Pendrel after all, one of yours, though of mamma's own recognised blood too, who came out as if on purpose to make the trouble among us; the trouble we doubtless needn't go into again now, even if it seems to have been thought as ill as possible of at the time."

"No, we needn't go into that of course," Ralph smiled—smiled verily through his exhilarated sense that whereas the best of reasons for their not doing so would have dwelt a few moments before in his imperfect grasp of that affair, he now enjoyed the superior view of it as well before him and only a bit embarrassing to handle. "You didn't like us then, and we must have been brought up not greatly to like you—all the more even, no doubt, if we were in the wrong," he cleverly put it; "so that things got worse, and we thought still more evil, on both sides, than there *was* to think; which perhaps didn›t matter, nevertheless,» he added, «when once all commerce was quite broken off. Nothing can have passed between us, I make out, for at least twenty years; during which"—for that also came to him—"we lost every remnant of the credit originally enjoyed with you all by the stiffness of our stand on your side during the dreadful War."

She took this from him with a clear competence that yet didn't belittle his own—though his own, it might be added, was to indulge, the very next thing, in a throb of finer complacency. She stared a moment before saying, as she did with much point, that she hadn't heard of any American who when their capital fell before the British arms had given *them* any credit for anything; on which remark he commented in turn, smiling at what she appeared to have meant. «Don›t you happen to have heard, my dear, of the great revolutionary struggle with your poor mad old king, now at his last gasp as they tell me, through which my country won the independence it enjoys?"

He thought he had never in life seen anything handsomer than the way Miss Midmore had of tossing her head with a spirit and an air that might have been partly a fruit of breeding and partly an extravagance of humour. It made him note even at the moment that he had really in New York never seen a head prescriptively tossed, or never at least with that high grace; in spite of its being withal supposed there that the young American ladies were unsurpassed in their frank pretension to consequence. "We haven't forgotten how dreadfully ill you all behaved long ago," were the words with which she met this reflection on her intelligence; "but it's lucky for you that you had made overtures—to ourselves here I mean—before we came to blows with you again a few years since."

"I see, I see—friendly assurances had passed; so friendly that when the public breach was healed there was very little of the private left to be patched up with it." He rendered this justice to her not having gone so astray. "But I think the great thing must have been that I myself, such as you see me, don't remember the time when I didn't fairly languish for the sight of you. I mean," he explained, "for a view of London and of the dear old country—which my grandparents, you understand, when here in 1806 and lay it on as they would, I know, couldn't write home to us flattering enough accounts of."

"It was in 1807, if you please," Molly Midmore said, "and it was that visit of theirs, in which they showed such a desire to be civil, that began the great difference of which you and I enjoy at last the full advantage. They must have done very well," she next declared, "seeing the small cause we had to make much of you. They showed how they wished to change that and did their utmost for it. It was afterwards remembered among us that they had taken great pains."

"Yes indeed, they *would* have wanted to smooth down any awkwardness,» Ralph gaily returned; while the mere saying it made him within the moment see much beyond that supposititious truth, see everything exactly as it had happened. So very much thus emerged to distinctness, so much more than he could have gone into just then even hadn't she, in her way, apparently wished to produce a signal fact before he might, as he would perhaps have said, get in. He got in none the less now with another assured hit. "The notion of our coming together in this way was the best of what they had left behind them when they went off again: *that* was the real beginning, as you say, of your and my happiness that›s to be.»

She made less and less scruple of showing him how he charmed and amused. "The only thing is that they could scarce have plotted that out before either of us was born. I don't exaggerate my youth," said Molly, "since I've waited for you till now. But I'm not so old as that they could have told by the sight of me that you were going to grow up so certain to like me."

“I think *I* could have told it, my dear, even at the hour of my birth. At any rate,» Ralph laughed, «it was a fancy I took to as soon as it was ever mentioned to me——!»

“Which it can’t have been,” she broke in, “before a little more was known about your servant, sir, than you would seem to allow for, even granting she’s the wonder you behold!”

“I beheld the wonder, and I took it completely in,” Ralph instantly answered, “the minute I clapped eyes on the elegant portrait that reached us in New York some time back, of course—yet so lately as to show you all in your present bloom.” On his reference to which valuable object there befell him something he might have noted as more remarkable than whatever else had most seemed so, save that each improvisation, as he might fairly have called them all, gave way without fear to the brightening of further lights. Had he expressed at the very moment what hovered there before him he would have called it the gleam of an uncertainty on his young woman’s part as to whether, or at least as to when, she had sat for the picture the truth of which was so present to him. He might have caught her in the act of not acknowledging his reference—which it was somehow fortunate for her, wasn’t it? that she nevertheless didn’t repudiate before he had carried his hand to the inner left pocket of his coat and drawn out in its red morocco case the miniature that was to confirm his words. He had looked at her hard, as to hold her while he made sure of this, and the eyes that met his own, for the space of five seconds, wondered, not obscurely, if he were going to; after which, at the mere feel of the thing in his hand, his lips couldn’t help closing an instant as for giddiness, the positive swing of the excitement that declined so to fail. It was at each stroke as if he were treating himself to a wanton degree of it without the least menace of a penalty. Aren’t we perhaps able to guess that he felt himself for the ten elapsing seconds the most prodigious professor of legerdemain likely ever to have existed?—and even though an artist gasping in the act of success. The consciousness of that force took a fresh flight on the spot—it meant so the revelation of successes still to come. This particular one triumphed over the ambiguity in the girl’s face which had not immediately yielded to his gesture—but which did yield, he beautifully found, on his handing her the morocco case open and without his having himself so much as dropped his eyes on it. The intoxication of mere happy tact might really have paralysed in him for the moment any other sense. Yes, he extraordinarily felt, it was happy tact that made the object in his pocket respond to the fingers suddenly seeking it—and this, all so wonderfully, before they had either given it notice or received notice from it. It wasn't exactly success, no doubt, that he next imputed to his friend—since success with *her*, the success under which recognition, on her first glance at the offered picture, played straight out of her, would clearly have had to represent a triumph over truth, a pretence of recollection, instead of, as in this case, the very finest coincidence with it. "Oh yes, *that* picture!» Molly at once exclaimed, much as if her beauty had been often portrayed, and with the addition, the next instant, that they hadn't at home held the artist, for whom she quite remembered sitting, to have done her much justice; so that indeed, as she now made out, her mother must have sent the thing off without her being herself in the secret. "It's well enough," she went on, her handsome head just tipping to consider; "but if your mamma had sent us such a bungle as a likeness of *you*, my dear, I should have been in less hurry, I think, to make your precious acquaintance. It wasn't very gallant," she further splendidly observed, "that you should have needed a trumpery proof of what's thought of me while I on my side was ready to take you on trust!"

Nothing could have exceeded for him meanwhile the luxury of increase for what he might have called the filling-in of his fortune; odd enough though it still might be to hang with her thus over a gage which at the end of a minute she handed back to him, the case closed, under her light thumb, with a snap, and which he restored to his bosom with an air that perhaps carried off but imperfectly his not having desired to refresh his own eyes with the painter's presentation. Not till afterwards had he, for all his confirmed elation, high spirits enough to ask himself why he would so singularly have hated to put the content of the neat pair of covers to any ocular test. A content bravely attested after all by his companion they indubitably had; which inscrutable fact still so sufficed him, even at the later hour we mention, that his thumb ignored any itch to press the small clasp again. By that time he might have recalled how little he had been aware of the miniature against his breast before its being there was in so odd a fashion disclosed; with its coming back to him as well that his unawareness might have struck the girl herself, and not less, at any rate, that he had noted their flushing together under the force of something tacit, something that wasn't quite, that wasn't verily at all, in their speech. He was nevertheless for the present not to review any one of the felicities that more and more assured his steps, and that still made him, in living them over, catch his breath a little, he was not to recur to them without a finer and finer joy, without a positive pride, in the growth of his wit. It had broken out quite brilliantly, this wit, in that production of the morocco case, and what had it done less with his finding the very rightest terms for putting it, while Molly listened, that if he hadn't been able to repay in kind the compliment of her beautiful offering this was because the kind, the article worth her acceptance, was alas not produced in America? He was later on to remember indeed how she had answered with a frankness scarce failing of provocation that since he himself had been produced the country didn't at least lack fine material; with which too she had carried it off quite on his own level by making the point that the real repair of his neglect would be to sit as soon as possible to one of the great London hands. There were plenty to choose from, he would see, as he would see many other things that might be new to him; and wasn't it certain moreover that the fancy would then be—from the moment he humoured it, that is—not for a trifle to be carried about in a pocket, but for something of a style and size to hang there roundabout them, where it would have for company as many Pendrels as Midmores? These lively impressions were, as we say, inevitably to renew their edge, even if the sense of living to the increase of danger, or in other words to the increase of interest, rather swept away in its pulses any occasion to brood. It is nevertheless not with his eventual commentary on this course that we are concerned, so much as with the freshness of those first moments. It belonged on the spot to still another of them that he found occasion to take her up somehow, in all good faith and good humour, on that oddity she had appeared to let fall, the matter of Mrs. Midmore's being so in fear of her as to have had to make a secret of despatching the morocco case.

"We rather suppose over there, you know," he mentioned, "that in England at least the children are bred to such submission that the parents haven't to conspire for freedom behind their backs. And, to tell you all," he further explained, "we have thought of your mother as such a very high lady that to make our image fit the facts we must apparently think of *you* as a higher.»

"Do you consider," the girl asked at this, "that you've met me with such extraordinary signs of awe? I won't pretend indeed I'm a bleating lamb—but you'll see for yourself that, though we're remarkably alike, I think, and have both plenty of decision, or call it even temper, there's between us an affection stronger even than our force of will on either side and which has always kept difficulties down. She happens to like what I like, just as I want to like, being so fond of her, what she does—though I don't say that if that were different there wouldn't be a touch of strife. If we've the same spirit therefore we've luckily for the most part the same tastes—which I dare say I wouldn't tell you, however, if I thought you'd be afraid of me for 'em. For all my boldness, at the same time, and which I come as honestly by as you will, I'd never look at a man of whom I shouldn't myself once in a while be afraid. Unless you're prepared, sir, properly to make me so," she laughed, "we may therefore perhaps have gone too far—for mamma herself, in this, I think, would be as disappointed as I am."

"I don't care a bit how far we've gone," Ralph answered with the richest resolution, "since the more of you all I please, no doubt, and putting any fierceness quite aside, the better it will be for our union. You don't expect me to agree to terrorise you, I suppose," he pursued with ease, "and I shall defy you to prove to me that if I suit you it won't be because I'm amiable." With which he stood ever so masterfully smiling at her.

"Oh indeed I can see you're amiable!" she cried with joy.

"I'll be hanged," he declared, quite keeping up his tone, "if I'll take the trouble ever to be anything else! I've the assurance to say that you must take me exactly as I am."

"Why what in the world do I want of you but that you should show assurance? Isn't it what I just said?—and if people don't find you ready for them, when I love you for your readiness," she cried, "I think I shall box their ears."

"Oh I shall take care for them, poor wretches," he laughed, "that they shan't be caught doubting me; since you must remember, you see, that what I've most of all come over for is peace all round." He held her so perfectly now, he seemed to know, beyond any possible slip, that putting his hands again on her shoulders scarce made it the surer. She was nevertheless in them, under their particular pressure, more and more deeply, and it made for his gravely going on, while he kept her at the distance that seemed to leave them each space and sense for a consideration all but unspeakable: "Let us once more therefore, dearest, exchange the kiss of peace."

She closed her eyes upon him, and it was as if that consenting motion were one with the spring of his closer possession. This sweetness, renewed, held them together for a time he couldn't have measured, and which might have lasted longer but that he of a sudden knew, by the very beat of her heart, that something more had happened for him and that she was again in charge of it, as she had been at first. But it didn't make her let him go—which was the greatest of the wonders, and it hung there behind him, and without his wanting at once to turn, that another person had joined them who divided now Molly's attention and whom she bravely addressed. "Mr. Pendrel, you see, has come, and is giving us the kiss of peace."

II

Ralph was afterwards to make sure that he had heard Mrs. Midmore's voice before he saw her face, and that his young friend must accordingly so have detained him as that the new mistress of the scene enjoyed the fullest exhibition to sight of what her daughter announced to hearing. "Well I'm sure then I'm ready to receive it too when you've both had enough of it!"—this high clear tone fell on our young man's ear and constituted at a stroke, without the aid of his in the least otherwise taking her in, his first impression of Mrs. Midmore. It was anything but the voice of alarm, and yet was as fine as a knife-edge for cutting straight into his act of union with the girl. Never had he heard a human sound so firm at once and so friendly, so rich in itself and so beautiful, and at the same time raising so the question of whom it could be used by and what presence it denoted. He was of course informed of these matters the next instant or as soon as he could turn in the disengaged way. But the few seconds had already sufficed; they gave him as nothing previous had done the note and measure of the close social order into which he had plunged, so that in facing his proper hostess he had already winced as at the chill of a tremendous admonition. Molly, during his passage with her, had, whether wittingly or no, left him unwarned and unscared; but the fashion after which her fine smiling parent both made good the fairest predictions and threatened instant confusion was as great a puzzle as, with time for it, a rash gentleman could have wished to handle. There she was, the very finest woman of her age possible, as Miss Midmore, for comparison, was the very finest of hers, but all to the instant effect of having made him just by her few words say to himself that he had never in all his days before so much as heard personal speech, and wonder in consequence what such a speaker would make of his own. The marvel was for the moment that with her handsome hard face brightened up for him not less clearly than a badge of importance, on occasion laid by, is judiciously polished for wearing, she should expose her sensibility, or in other words her social surface, to what his native expression might have at the best to treat it to. The marvel was indeed that, borrowing as she did he could scarce have said what air of authority, verily of high female office, from her rich-looking black attire, she determined in him even before he had spoken an inward gasp of confession. "I'm a rank barbarian, yes: she must, oh she *must*, take me for that!"—he put this to himself at that instant with a kind of plea for his greater ease. It came to him that since he couldn't possibly succeed with her as a fine gentleman—even though, so oddly, he appeared to have succeeded as such with her daughter—his advantage would be in some quite other wild grace, on which therefore he must desperately throw himself.

However, she was herself an apparition of such force that the question of his own luck missed application and he but stared at her lost, and yet again lost, in that reflection that yes, absolutely yes, no approach to such a quality of tone as she dealt in had ever in his own country greeted his ear. Yes, again and yet again, it spoke of ten thousand things that he could guess at now in her presence, and that he had even dreamed of, beforehand, through faint echoes and in other stray lights; things he could see she didn't in the least think of at the moment either, all possessed as she was with the allowance she had in her hospitality already made for him. Every fact of her appearance contributed somehow to this grand and generous air, the something-or-other suggesting to him that he had never yet seen manner at home at that pitch, any more than he had veritably heard utterance. When or where, in any case, had his eye, alert as he might feel it naturally was, been caught by such happy pomp as that of the disposed dark veil or mantilla which, attached to her head, framed in hoodlike looseness this seat of her high character and, gathering about her shoulders, crossed itself as a pair of long ends that depended in lacelike fashion almost to her feet? He had apprehended after a few more seconds that here was "costume" beheld of him in the very fact and giving him by its effect all the joy of recognition—since he had hitherto had but to suppose and conceive it, though without being in the effort, as his own person might testify, too awkwardly far out. Yes, take him for what she would, she might see that he too was dressed—which tempered his barbarism perhaps only too much and referred itself back at all events, he might surely pretend, to a prime and after all not uncommendable intuition of the matter. If he had always been, as he would have allowed, overdressed for New York, where this was a distinct injury to character and credit, business credit at least, which he had none the less braved, so he had already found he was no more than quite right for London, and for Mansfield Square in especial; though at the same time he didn't aspire, and wouldn't for the world, to correspond with such hints as Mrs. Midmore threw off. She threw it off to a mere glance that she represented by the aid of dress the absolute value and use of presence as presence, apart from any other office—a pretension unencountered in that experience of his own which he had yet up to now tended to figure as lively. Absolutely again, as he could recover, he had never understood presence without use to play a recognised part; which would but come back indeed to the question of what use—great ambiguous question-begging term!—might on occasion consist of. He was not to go into that for some time yet, but even on the spot it none the less shone at him for the instant that he was apparently now to see ornament itself frankly recognised as use; and not only that, but boldly

contented, unassailably satisfied, with a vagueness so portentous—which it somehow gave a promise to his very eyes of the moment that he should find convincingly asserted and extended. All this conspired toward offering him in this wondrous lady a figure that made ladies hitherto displayed to him, and among whom had been several beauties, though doubtless none so great as splendid Molly, lose at a stroke their lustre for memory, positively vitiated as they thus seemed by the obscurity, not to say the flat humility, of their employed and applied and their proportionately admired state.

We hasten to concede of course that Ralph entered in those few instants but into imperfect possession of the excited sense, the glimpse of more and more great things, provoked for him by his elder kinswoman's resonant arrival; yet it's no extravagance to say that the knowledge Molly had been teaching him he was already master of took a measureless bound with the act of his just kissing Mrs. Midmore's hand. She let him do this as a first sequel to her remark on her daughter's description of their commerce, but his own next consciousness was that of being kissed by her on both cheeks—he could scarce have said whether more freely or more nobly: the first sequel would have been poor without the second, she struck him as having at once admonished him, leaving on his hands his quick conception of how he should act with true elegance, the style of behaviour on which she would generally speaking most reckon. He had never before kissed a lady's hand, nor seen one kissed, save in a stage-play; also the way he did it would stamp him the barbarian she had disposed him, under the rush of his perceptions, to seek his best safety in proving himself: yet it was to become at the end of a minute a consequence of these things that he felt to the full how soundly Molly had answered for his freedom to fear nothing. This he so succeeded in achieving by the aid of the ladies conjoined that he could scarce have said when it was that his relation with the elder, now admirably sealed, had fitted him to distinctness with a fresh pair of wings and showed him there was no length to which they mightn't bear him. How had this fond presumption grown, he might afterwards have wondered, unless by just listening to her voice of voices?—her beautiful bold tone simply leading the way, as he subsequently made the matter out, and his ear, all but irrespective of its sense, holding and holding it, indifferent for the hour to what it meant, and yet withal informed, by its mere pitch and quality, of numberless things that were to guard him against possible mistakes, very much as he had been guarded during his passage with Molly. Numberless things, yes; so many that he was afterwards to see how he owed all those he could feel most at his ease about to this extraordinarily fortifying hour. He might afterwards make out that it had been fortifying, at least in part, because it had been so flattering: he soon ceased to care that he was after all apparently not able to pass for a barbarian—his connection with the secure world, that of manners and of every sort of cross-reference, that of the right tone and the clear tradition, had been settled at every point at which equivocation would otherwise have waited. If it wasn't flattering that two such women should have made him by a turn of the hand their very own and have opened out to him, without a shade of reserve that he could catch in the fact, every privilege thereunto attached, there was no sense in the great mystifying term, as he had always found it, which resembled the custom of hand-kissing in that he had hitherto known it but by name. To taste of the sweet was to feel sure he had gone to this hour without it, just as on his side he had never helped another to it—no, not in the least after the fashion according to which he had let his present companions, and Mrs. Midmore of course in especial, hand it forth as in a deep-bowled silver spoon.

What overtook him further withal, a few moments later, was that if he shouldn't be able to keep it down the measure of his new luxury might so keep itself up as to overstrain all their powers, his own stomach for it not least: the near danger of this topple seemed in fact presented to him as soon as a third member of the family had been admitted by the door of Mrs. Midmore's entrance—the servant who had waited on his own now passing in again as if to clear the approach and make another announcement. The footman in effect said nothing, or nothing at least was heard by Ralph, who was struck at once with this young man's almost wild sidelong stare at him, a positively droll departure from the strict servile propriety the fellow seemed otherwise formed to express, and with the way the gentleman so ushered in pulled up before a bolder approach and stood testifying, as might have seemed, to a form of apprehension scarce more happily controlled. The fresh apparition, it was easy to see, could be but a Midmore of Midmores; which was doubtless in great part why his arrest, his frightened bulging eyes, his immediate failure of assurance, where assurance, by Ralph's conception, would so have consorted, represented the honest tribute of a person hugely impressed. Our own young man's high accessibility to impressions on his side, and all, however quickly multiplied, kept separate in spite of their number, showed him during the minute that ensued quite half-a-dozen different things of the first importance—such as that Mrs. Midmore must promptly have spoken, must have said something like "Oh Perry dear, don't hang back; come and bid our great cousin welcome!" such as that, for all the pitch of her flattery, as the scene fairly flushed with it, she didn't like her son quite so artlessly to gape, preferring, for herself, more intention and thereby, as it were, more profit; such as that, at the same time, Perry Midmore, whose name of Peregrine our remarkable friend immediately fixed on him, had quite other signs than those of general, of easy or precipitate deference. Short and sturdy, stocky, as Ralph, reproducing the image, might have described him, he was so stout and direct an assertion of ready brute force that his air of misgiving, his confession of shyness, his discountenanced first looks at the possible adversary awaiting him might, on the ground of any comparison of matter with mind, quite have gone to that adversary's head. Tight in his clothes, especially in the buckskin breeches which his riding-boots surmounted almost to the knee and his stout legs exposed to a strain; tight in his vividly blue coat, which had a tail but no skirts, though indeed brass buttons galore, as if to make up for that, and which suggested at the wrists, under the arms and across the chest, that he might fairly have outgrown it through daily increase of strength; tight even in the redundant neckcloth that couldn't well have strangled him, and yet above which his young face and the large fold of his chin, in particular, declared themselves purple and congested—carrying out also, with the fine bright sheen of the skin, that betrayal as of a general tense surface and of the effect of breathing hard beneath it. Ralph was afterwards thoroughly to learn both how far the fortitude of this nominal young head of the house of Midmore could go and where and why it would fail; but the immediate exhibition was that of an extraordinary diffidence, almost a chill of fear, in face of the unusual. This let our friend see, out of hand, how new and how strange he must have struck his kinsman as being, in spite of such preparations as must already have worked for him; which fact it was—just the primitive candour of Perry's revelation—that most impressed on him his fine liability to loom large.

It wouldn't be a great affair, certainly, to loom large to Perry—that he at once grasped; for while he felt himself thus play on his sensibility he felt sure that all there might be of that article, absolutely all, was engaged, with nothing left over for any other use—though this apprehension, at the same time, clothed the odd figure with a richer interest perhaps than any yet stirring in his breast. Perry would be bold, Perry would be brave, would be even, and with the last unconsciousness, brutal; and withal for those lapsing moments Perry would have given anything not to have to deal with a presence that deprived him at a stroke of those of his advantages, as he knew these, that had accompanied him up to the very door. Ralph felt in the full measure of this perception the desire he should keep them, and for the very fullest exhibition;

which he would be hanged if he didn't positively *make* him do—so that to begin this effect on the spot he smiled and smiled, smiled verily as perhaps never in his life before, and alas but at first with the apparent consequence of inspiring more mistrust. It was probably at this instant that there fell upon our friend the first light sense of a predicament on his own part the gravity of which he was before long not to mistake—the faintest symptomatic hint, that is, of a dilemma so extraordinary that we shall scarcely be able to do it justice enough, consisting as it did in the prevision of his probable failure to keep himself unperturbed, in the right proportion, by the mistrust it was open to him, on a certain side, or at least in certain quarters, to inspire. Why should he, why should he? he was to be able to say to himself, though indeed after much else had happened, that he had then inwardly and rather sickishly begun to inquire; for in the least degree to determine wonderments that should be beyond answering was the last thing he had dreamed of, and we may in fact all but feel his heart even now stand still for half a second under that noted first breath of a fear. That he wanted but to please and soothe and satisfy him, that he was ready to sacrifice to so doing all but the blood of his veins, this came over him to the point of bringing out sweat-drops on his brow while he met his kinsman's bulging eyes with the grace of reassurance we have just imputed to his own. He understood, he understood—which was the challenging interest: Perry scented his cleverness, so to call it, scented his very act of understanding, as some creature of the woods might scent the bait of the trapper; whereby it was that to prosecute success by wiles more manifest yet and then but watch them brilliantly fail might well mean at last finding no issue in a case that depended on issues. Was this perfect example of whatever he should really prove—his absolute transparency making him preciously perfect—going to defeat by mere alarm the true, the extreme felicity of a right relation with him? that relation which would consist of seeing how he was shut up to his three or four parts as to the rooms of a house of three or four windows and only a bolted door, and attending him there with the due allowance for this. The point would be in the young man's dim perception and possible resentment of allowances—conceivably productive in him of positive unrest; thanks, no less conceivably, to his being probably as neat a case as one could desire of impenetrable density before the unfamiliar. The unknown, however presented to him, would remain for him the unknowable, and by just so much the detestable and the impossible, calling on quasi-brutish instincts of danger and self-defence. The danger would be to the element of pride in him, one of the three or four properties that a Midmore had easily at hand, and that could quite naturally make the embodiment of such a privilege recognise whatever might menace it, even though with no resource or comfort in the matter but a dull direct hate, a straight if unpolished arm.

To divine these things, however, was also, while one was about it, to divine the presence, lurking among them, of the question of calculable profit, the power, elementary enough, to compare inconveniences and choose the least—the greatest being of course the one that would most interfere with such a gentleman's material ease. It was solid, it had always been, to be a Midmore of Drydown—that pressed heavier upon Ralph each instant; but the virtue of the solid was exactly that you couldn't see through it, as you might, or as unmannerly people at least, looking hard at it, might, should financial inanition begin to make it at all thin. Horrid for the great—since, strangely enough, the young man, staring, lowering, vainly dissimulating, or at least ineffectually pretending, did in his way represent greatness—to have to feel less at home in the world, or certainly in Mansfield Square, let alone at Drydown itself, by the want of anything their quality had learned from such a good way back to take for granted. Our friend vibrated to the sense of still another tenth of a second during which the measure of the want he himself was to supply made him blink as by its intense flash, directly after which he knew that his gallantry of welcome to Perry, his smile of intelligence—he might fairly have damned the intelligence he couldn't keep down!—was practically a suggestion that his cousin should advance and receive his promise to pay. His cousin did advance, at the worst, more rapidly than any effective alarm of Ralph's on this score could supervene; and then the latter scarce knew what brave distance had been covered by the exchange between them of a fine old fraternal embrace over which Mrs. Midmore's authority, dominant really, after all, through everything, had somehow presided with elegance and yet without ceremony.

Was it the fact of the embrace, was it the common stout palpability, the very human homely odour, of his relative, that had at the end of a minute dispelled all difficulties and renewed the wonderful rush, as it could only be felt, of the current? Certain it was that if Perry was going to be curious, and this most perhaps by the repudiation in him of the very rudiments of curiosity, so at the same time he had become as a creature to play with—from the moment at least of one's having something to his advantage to dangle before him. His human simplicity would surely mark itself as unlike, as quite beyond, anything of the sort that had ever confronted Ralph with pretensions or assumptions; and how should that alone not prove tempting to one's taste for a game, exasperated as this taste might become by such particular stupidities of confidence and comfort as would inevitably await it? It might be indeed that one had never seen the straight force of stupidity so attested—that straight force being, when applied, nothing very much other than brutality; which, clearly, lurked here with supports and accessories and surrounding graces, the fair and delicate house, the full-voiced mannerly women, the ordered consideration of twenty kinds, that it was so far from being able to draw upon in a country where it was mainly known but by its going naked and unashamed. Ralph easily knew that the attempt to preserve itself there in whatever approach to the conditions now before him would have had overmuch to reckon with distraction and diversion. All of which wondrous interpretation, on his part, of the few trifles light as air that achieved in as few seconds such a brushing of his sense, left him momentarily with a tight hold of Perry's hand and an ear still reached by his hard breathing—this too though the return to their orbits of his silly scared eyes was more assured.

Ralph further knew a desire to mark the distinction between being satisfied of him and amused at him, and was aware above all of something sharper for the instant than aught else, the fixed and extreme attention of the others, the look of the two ladies at their son and brother as if under stress of what they might gain or lose by the sentiment he should provoke; their major care for *that*, in the connection, rather than for their visitor's own immediate action, enriching again in our young man the savour of success. It was as Molly's husband to be, who had just arrived from America to claim her hand, and who had in fact just claimed it and felt it brightly conferred, along with a fond mother's blessing, by the grand girl herself—it was under instruction to greet him in this character that he knew Perry to have been pushed into his arms; and what with the lapse of the next minute had come to hang in the balance was whether or no that youth, the head of the family but also the fool of it, and with some rude art of his own the will of it, would stand out for his right not to have been passed over by the offhand transaction. He was a gentleman to stand out for his rights up to any point at which he shouldn't get bewildered about them; for he was also a gentleman to get bewildered, that is easily to be determined in such a sense, on any ground not absolutely to be felt by the shuffle of his feet. In saying to him with fine gaiety "I want to commend myself all round, and quite understand that I must before the last word is said—so that you must give me time for it a bit, please:" in saying, in risking, he verily felt, as much as this he would have been conscious of more felicity had he not seen the very next instant that gaiety might well be too fine to please in the difficult relation; to which it would thus appear that his kinsman could only contribute in highest measure a mistrust of any semblance of manner, or at least of such manner as a glib adventurer from overseas might have brought with him. He was probably formed not to "like" manner, or to understand it, whether kept up or kept down, damn him; for if Ralph, with his own splendid sense for rising again to the surface after deep submersions, could take the quickest conceivable note of this, so there hung in his eye at the same time the lively truth, which fairly jerked out arms and legs like those of a toy harlequin worked by a string, that manner was essentially and by an extraordinary law to be his constant resort and weapon and of consistent application to every aspect of his case. It wouldn't of course always be the same, nor would he wish it to, since that would represent the really mad grimace; but the vision of it was precious in proportion as he felt how, so remarkably, in fact so unaccountably, he should need always to work from *behind* something—something that, look as it would, he must object to Perry›s staring at in return as if it were a counterfeit coin or a card from up his sleeve.

Let us frankly plead, for that matter, that he found himself affected before this passage lapsed as by the suddenest vision of a possibility of his having to appeal from the imputation, as who should say, of cheating, cheating in that sense which his above-mentioned love of the game, exactly, might expose him to suspicion of; this for all the world as if he were seated with the house of Midmore, not to speak of other company too, at a green table and between tall brave candlesticks which would at a given moment somehow perversely light the exchange of queer glances from partner to partner at his expense. So odd an apprehension could cast of course but the briefest shade: breath after breath and hint after hint—though whence directed who should say?—so spending themselves upon the surface of his sensibility that impressions, as we have already seen, were successively effaced and nothing persisted but the force of derived motion. As soon as he had heard his affianced bride, for instance, take up with infinite spirit the words of accommodation just addressed by him to her brother he seemed to see a shining clearance and to measure the span by which the three of them together, he and she and her mother, would be cleverer than any home criticism. "What puts it into your head, please, that if I'm quite content, and bold enough into the bargain to say as much to whomever it may concern, what puts it into your head that he may have a case against you that need give you the least trouble?" She spoke that out like her mother's daughter, whether like her brother's sister or no, blooming with still greater beauty and so attracting and holding Perry's eyes in consequence that when he turned them back again they reflected something of her pride.

"There's not a gentleman too grand for her anywhere," her brother observed to Ralph; "but I suppose you think yourself quite one of ourselves; which I don't say you're not," he added with due caution, "if you really please her and please my mother, to say nothing——"

"To say nothing of my pleasing you, of course"—Ralph took him up with the address that, however it might turn, he would so assuredly have to make the best of. "Yes, that's of course, but I won't pretend I don't draw a great confidence from their favour: I've felt them on the spot just as wise as they are kind. Just as kind as they are handsome too," he went on, looking at his kinsman ever so much harder and harder—which he somehow found that, though it wasn't at all what he wanted, he couldn't in the least help. It made him drive his address home, and this was, in the oddest way, as if he had his host by the body in a sort of intimate combat and were trying him and squeezing him for a fall. Perry would have to *take* him, and to show that he had taken him—this was the tug; only the more he conveyed that, even if he wreathed it, so to say, in flowers and the more he thereby insisted on a relation, if not on the one, the more he seemed to give his man an opportunity the other aspect of which was that it was for himself a form of exposure. Why he should be exposed, and what, above all, exposed to, was more than he could have said—wondering as he did at this even while a passion urged and an instinct warned him. There it was, in any case: he couldn't help *sounding* Perry, even in the presence of the women; which was what brought upon him, through concentration of the visual sense, the challenge he seemed positively to advance into the enemy›s county in order to invite. It was the rate at which he drew intelligence out of the dull that made him uneasy when it ought to have made him, by every presumption, feel it as wind in his sails. Violating nature, as might fairly seem, in the face before him, what was such a glimmer intelligence *of*?—this he asked himself while he watched it grow and while, into the bargain, he might have marvelled at the oddity of one's wanting to be impressive without wanting to be understood. To be understood simply as impressive—it was this that would best consort; but what the devil wouldn't requiring such a creature to be more penetrable perhaps represent in the way of teaching it tricks it might use against one? In the act of impressing, Ralph felt, he encouraged familiarity—which was what people had been known to do at their cost and to the provocation of bad accident by putting primitive natures in a false position. False indeed would be the position when Perry should begin, say, to know more about Ralph Pendrel than this lover of life knew about himself. It may be added that if these considerations did lurk in the expression of countenance bent by Ralph upon his host with general ingenious intent, even a Midmore stuffed with a single prejudice might well have picked from the bunch some hint of a sinister menace to that monotony.

"You don't mean to say you're struck with *my* appearance—I know it›s not my strong point!» Perry said goodhumouredly enough, after all, and with a laugh which put that quantity at once in a better light. «But I like, as much as you please, to be praised for what I *am*" he added—"if you'll give me time to show that; for I suppose you've already noticed that in this country we *take* time for our affairs, and perhaps no people among us all more than we of this family; which has gone on for ever so long, yon know, at its own pace and never allowed itself to be driven. We probably don't *look* to you, however, as if you could lash us up—out of breath even as you may perhaps be with your errand; and that›s all the appearance I pretend to make to anyone. What I leave to my mother I do leave to her," the young man further declared—more and more articulate, clearly, on finding himself so well listened to; "and of course she and Miss Midmore are as clever as they're handsome, if that's what you want." After achieving, with some unexpectedness for Ralph, this effort of propriety, he looked as in recovered self-possession from Mrs. Midmore to Molly, and then again very hard at his sister and back at his mother, so that it shouldn't be his fault, obviously, if they didn't trust his tact. He showed himself in short the man of sense and of consequence, though while speaking he had stared straight before him, not resting his eyes on Ralph, who, none the less, at once and cordially welcomed his remarks.

"I hear you with the greatest interest, but even if we don't always take time enough in America for what we do, I'm not going to grant you that I haven't thoroughly thought of what I'm about in coming to you. And if you care to know it," Ralph continued, "it has taken but four days of old England to convince me that you're the happiest people in the most convenient country. I've been since I landed more pleased and amused than I can tell you." With which our young man again smiled and smiled.

"Oh you've seen nothing as yet compared to what you will," Mrs. Midmore impatiently broke in—"and I know," she said, "that what Perry would like to say to you is that you'll have no idea of anything till you've seen and admired Drydown. That you shall do in good time—it's a place I shall make it *my* care that you shall get to love, for that's where we're at home, where we're *what* we are, if you understand; and where, as I see Perry desires to assure you, you shall have a horse of your own to ride, and the best home-grown victual that you›ll anywhere find to eat, and a capital neighbourhood to receive civility from, to say nothing of one of the very finest views in England spread out before you."

"You shall have any horse that you can ride," Perry concurred, his clue to amiability now quite grasped, with this fine example of it given; "though it isn't when they're most to my taste, I grant, that they're apt to be most to other men's. That's what I say to my friends"—and he improved his theme, not to speak of his himself improving with it: "I tell 'em they're welcome to any mount that suits 'em, and I don't think I find it in general a freedom from which my animals suffer. Unless it be," he pursued, appealing again with his flushed but comparatively directed deliberation to his sister, "unless it be that I provide better still for Molly's liking—since I must make him understand, you know," he kept on, "how straight he has to follow if he's so bold as to allow you a lead."

"I'm sure I hope he'll be bold enough to ride with his wife!" the girl splendidly laughed—"or, if you think I put it too forwardly, with a young lady whom he has in half an hour inspired with such kindness that she wouldn't for the world do him a mite of harm." There was that in her free archness which struck again for Ralph the note of he could scarce have said what old-time breadth of the pleasant address and the frolic challenge; so that, sounded out in this way before the others, it made him pant a little as if he were in fact engaged in "following" and needed all his effort not to be left behind. He felt in comparison, before such a force of freshness, almost disembodied, and didn't know for a moment what he mightn't have said if she hadn't, still lighting the way for him with her great confident eyes, seemed to wish to give him all sorts of assurance in the single charge: "You're not to be afraid, you're not to be afraid——!"

"I hope to heaven I shan't let you see it if I am!" he interrupted. "And you and your brother must remember at any rate that though the natives of Mexico and Peru, when first discovered by the Spaniards, had never seen a horse and thought them very terrible, we have long ago got over that in our part of the country, and indeed, I think, are not much in fear of anything or anyone—unless it be perhaps of finer ladies than our simple society and our homely manners have yet taught us to deal with. I pray the powers," he went on to his kinsman, for whom once more, despite his desire to the contrary, he felt himself "figure" all too unavoidably and confoundingly, "I pray the powers I mayn't want either for wit or for any other sort of coolness when it's a question of your fine gentlemen—by which I mean of my enjoying their notice and letting them not doubt of mine. But of course my very errand shows you how marked I am for the full ravage of female loveliness and for the advantage that it gains from the perfect gentility waiting upon it among you here. It must clearly do what it will with me, you see, and if the best it can do is likely to be to kill me why I'll at least go merrily to my death."

Perry Midmore, listening to this, kept his face half averted, but his eye was now more judiciously watchful and he turned it askance in his attention. He would weigh things and be wise—they might help to make him so, when his visitor uttered them, if they couldn't always make him ready; all of which inward comment the visitor had again the vexed consciousness of not being able to keep him from suspecting. He had taught him within five minutes that there was, that there could be, such a thing, and its pointing itself at him, whatever its sense, was the new and the disquieting fact. Ralph laid a hand on his shoulder with a singular sudden impulse to prove that even if one's thought was at play, since this was on occasion of the perverse nature of thought, the letting it take its full course would really bring it round to a point, in fact to a succession of points, where another would recognise it as positively working for him; and the gesture did after an instant so far operate as that the other's queer little glare abated and he stood as stiffly passive as if, whatever this should mean, the least movement might perhaps precipitate some further complication.

Mrs. Midmore meanwhile, Ralph saw, had so completely measured his own bright promise that, quite at her ease about it, her anxiety was all for her son's somehow interfering with the prospect; which she at the same time mightn't be able to take him up upon by reason of something divinably new and strange, something perhaps even beyond his usual show of shyness and that provoked wonder at the cause of it. Ralph had in fact in this connection another of his sublime instants, as we may fairly call them, with this particular one possibly the most sublime—since her next motion, though but a momentary look at him, of the supremely searchingest, played straight out of her desire to side with him, as it were, against any hindrance to a right understanding and a convenient, an elegant smoothness that her boy should stupidly offer. Wasn't there in her face during the moment a dim glimmer of inquiry?—something like "What on earth *is* it, yes, that you›re doing to him, what was it, yes, a few minutes ago, when if I hadn›t been watching him he would have shuddered like a frightened horse who sniffs in the air the nearness of some creature of a sort he has never seen?" The whole mother would have been in that, Ralph was afterwards to make out, the mother deeply engaged for her daughter's benefit and pleasure, as well as for anything to the advantage of the race in general that could be picked up by a sufficiently dignified long arm, and at the same time so rich in instincts that had for their centre the prior consequence of the head of the house, that she could almost know alarm in the midst of jubilation, and at any rate seemed to turn upon the hero of the occasion, for the five seconds, the chill of a special quite tremendous suggestion. She wanted right resolutely to like and to further him—it would be so good for them all, and if he was destined in any degree to counter this it wouldn't be by an effect upon her directly produced, but literally through her fond attention to Perry and even should that attention amount to impatience of Perry's attitude. He would but have to show personal fear, so to call it, or perhaps to do no more than show that he was afraid in advance of knowing it, for that question of what might be the matter with him to lead to the other and the finer. Such might be taken then as the way in which the last wonder about the American cousin would doubtless usher itself in. It was, however, so far from having yet won an inch of the ground, or having indeed really foreshadowed its power to do this, that all Ralph knew, to the effect of joy, within the minute, was that she was just putting Perry as right as possible again by the renewed wealth of her tone.

"Don't turn it upon us that we take you for a savage," she laughed to her visitor, "when you talk about killing and dying among us as if we were Red Men on the war-path! If we're going to kill and eat you at any rate—isn't that what your cannibals do?—we shall at least fatten you first for the table, and you needn't fear but that you'll enjoy that as much as you may suppose us to enjoy, as good judges, the next stage of the affair. I'm an excellent judge myself, please believe, and I shall decline to have you despatched before you're in perfect condition. Meanwhile therefore," she nobly continued, "we shall live upon you in *this* pleasant way—and with Molly›s good right to be helped to you first, always first, entirety understood by us. The only thing is that I'm not sure we're quite eager to share you at once with a hundred other people."

Perry it was, rather remarkably, who spoke in answer to these fine words before Ralph had time to meet them—obliged as the latter always was, after all, to select a little among the resources of his wit. "Shan't you have a good bit to share him with my sister Nan at least?—*you*, I mean," he said to his mother, his hands in his pockets now and with the effect from it of a hunch up of his shoulders which at once established somehow his air of more conscious intention. "I don't say it for Molly, of whom I shouldn't expect it, and who of course will tear her sister's eyes out if Nan takes too much for granted. But you're kinder to Nan than Molly is," he continued—"and it's I," he still went on, with a turn now to their visitor, "it's I, among the three of us, that she can look to most. Oh yes," he persisted as for the benefit of the ladies, "you want him to know all about it, so I'm just telling him, don't you see? And it's what you yourself want to know, I take it, cousin—though I don't doubt of you as one for finding out."

He had grown of a sudden extraordinarily more assured, and Ralph, quite directly faced by him with it, felt at once how the interest of him was quickened. Catching the air of their faces he could note as well that Mrs. Midmore and Molly were not differently affected; which perception—and the two women exchanged at the moment a pair of quite confirmatory glances—renewed his sense that something unprecedented had within the ten minutes happened to Perry, and was indeed continuing to happen, just as he himself continued to have to recognise that he was, no comfort of responsibility, the author of it. Not only was this there, moreover, to strain further than would have in advance seemed possible the all-engaging smile into which he kept falling back for refuge, but it was also salient in the scene that however one might interpret such an exhibited phenomenon the character showing it was himself getting used to it; so that what had in truth most acutely taken place was that the worthy in question had of a sudden almost jumped to a vision of not suffering, or at any rate of not losing, by it. Whatever it might be, in fine, there was something to be done with it—as for instance that he should thrust it straight at Ralph in this account of embarrassing matters. Wasn't the point that he would make them embarrassing, damn him, if he could, and that, detected by his mother and sister, he was at the very stroke of trying it on? If the ladies would help the embarrassment not to act, Ralph inwardly remarked, the case would still have more of amusement than anything else to give out; only—*there* was the betrayal he seemed to catch—they might, for all one knew, presently find themselves not able to: which was perhaps exactly what had been meant by that tacit communication between them. "Nan is at Dry down, where I left her yesterday," Perry meanwhile went on to mention, "and would have liked beyond anything in life coming up to pay you her respects. But if you notice her delay in waiting on you my mother will explain with pleasure how many obligations she has at home—though I'll be hanged if I believe in them enough, ma'am, not to be sorry I didn't bring her to town, even if I had to put her up behind me on Rouser. She's not a girl who either mopes or rebels," he added for Ralph's benefit before his mother, taken by surprise, could meet these sudden freedoms; "but no more is she a household drudge or a mere milkmaid, and you're not to think that if she's kept at a distance it's because she's not fit to be seen. She's not a great toast like Molly, but she's much handsomer than I am, don't you think, ma'am?"—and with this he fairly advanced upon his mother, who still more markedly flushed at the style of his address. "If our cousin's to make our fortune," he wound up, "let him see as soon as possible how many he'll have to provide for."

"You've broken out into such cleverness, my lad, that you should certainly now be trusted to make your own!" Mrs. Midmore returned, the brightness of her dignity suffering a little, Ralph could see, yet being put to no great pains to carry itself off as untouched. "Should you wish to see poor Nan at once," she remarked to her visitor, "we can easily send for her by the coach, and then you can judge of what she costs me at least to keep!"

"Why don't you rather propose that he shall take the coach himself if it's such a cruelty to them to wait?" Molly asked of her mother, but rolling her fine eyes at Ralph in a manner that helped for the moment to make him feel more astray than any challenge to his perception had yet succeeded in doing. "So near a relation needn't fear any gossip, so that if you pay her a visit there it isn't I, sir," she laughed, "who shall feel a penny the worse. What in the world should my little sister be but his little sister too?—making it a new big brother, for herself, who may strike her indeed as a better fortune, not to call it even a better brother, than any she now can boast of. If you really want to go at once," she kept on to Ralph, and dropping him the smartest curtsey with it, "I'll trust you to come back to me in time—in time to marry me, I mean," she cried; "and I don't mind telling you that if you shouldn't I'd make no scruple of going to bring you. Nan is the nicest little body, and, with the gardener's wife to help, would make you, I think, comfortable enough."

On which extravagant dazzle of pleasantries she paused a moment, Ralph feeling the while that their being to such a tune mutually and, as he might have put it, crudely astare signified something that had not as yet come up between them. Oh they had been making and taking a prodigious amount of affectionate assurance, but didn't Ralph know on the spot, hadn't he in fact been advised for the last three minutes, that here was matter of intimacy beyond any token they had exchanged and a different sort of business altogether from even the sharpest need yet resting on him to patch up a sense? There had been none he didn't patch up with that effect as of a quick bright triumph over difficulty—so that we have repeatedly seen how the challenge to his awareness, when pressed, set that awareness on its feet in time, never failing after this fashion to save his confidence. What had now taken place was that unexpectedly his need seemed to betray instead of helping him: every blest reference save the present had in other words found him ready—and not just ready to show he knew, but ready quite to know; only this question of an identity thrust at him to which he couldn't rise and which didn't, like all the others, breathe on him after an instant the secret of the means of rising, only this one left him to direct at Molly (which came indeed to saying at their companions too) a smile which would turn really to sickness should it have to last but a moment longer. Stranger than anything yet for our young man was what now occurred: his getting as in the glimmer of a flash the measure of the wonders he had achieved, and getting it through this chill of the facility stayed. What made it a chill was the felt danger, drawn from her look, of Molly's speaking his case out at him before he could prevent her. "Why you don't know, truly you don't know, therefore what are you talking about?"—that was in her face or was on the point of being, and the great pang was that he minded it himself still more than she and the others certainly would if they should fairly detect it. He *didn't* know, he hadn›t known, and he wasn't going to or it would have come by this time: there wasn't in him the first faint possibility of an "Oh yes, your sister Nan of course, who is of such-and-such an age and such-and-such a figure and such-and-such a connection with the grand image of you that we've had at home!" There was no grand image, nor even any scantest, of a nice little body, as Molly had put it, lurking in the family background and as to whom, by the same magic of wanting to enough which had constantly served him, he could be sure he was passably provided. The possibility of sickness was in the fall from such a proved independence of the baseness, as who should say, of pretending. Two or three times, yes, it might have appeared he should have to pretend, some gap in his inspiration remaining too distinctly unbridged; but with that villainy *always* averted—since positively it wore the villain›s face—by its having become in the very nick the mere mistake of his fear. He had thus again and again escaped being too superficial, and with this gain of certitude of how little he was there to be so at all had come each time the sense of luxury in his renewals of recognition. That there would be no luxury in not recognising, his failure of vision in respect to a second daughter of the house instantly taught him, but even while it did so no repair of the lapse arrived.

What Molly saw, and what in ten seconds more she would make the others see, was the fact of the lapse unrelieved—the queerness of which for her was indeed already out with her asking him what was the matter and why in the world he looked at the mention of the dear thing at Drydown as if he were going to be ill. The extraordinary point of which withal was that she was herself ready the instant after to jump into detection verily, but detection of what wasn't—not at all of what was. His so helplessly hanging fire represented clearly, to her freshened perception, and thereby his own still sharper embarrassment, that he had been thinking more of poor Nan than of the rest of them put together; though of course when she brought her large irony to bear on this he could luckily snatch at his obvious retort and make his flushed laugh invite their companions to see how it righted him. "Did it strike you, my dear, that when I asked you a while since to take up with me for life I was really but expressing my interest in another person? If that was the case," he said to Mrs. Midmore and Perry, "I mean if I wasn't addressing her as an honest man—which she accuses me of—how could she guess it and yet at the same time make me such a blissfully happy one?" The question wasn't indeed in strictness for *them* to answer, and Molly, whatever they might have said, met it to her own sufficiency by another of her wondrous freedoms. «I could love you for a wretch, cousin, I think, as well as I could love you for a saint!" she cried; and it gave him at once, he seemed to feel, the luckiest chance for putting in his most vital plea.

"I don't care what you love me for if it's only as your very truest—and don't you see that when you doubt of my being so you deny by the same stroke that I'm the honest man I pretend?"

"Just listen to him, mother—was there ever anything grander than such a speech and such an air?" Her appeal was of the promptest, and if she addressed her parent her eyes took note but of her lover, whom, with her head inclined to one side, she might almost have been regarding in the light of a splendid picture. "I don't care, I don't care—it sets you off so to let me torment you. It's when I doubt of you," she said, "that you'll find me most adoring; and if you should ever dream I'm cold just draw me on to abuse you." She gave him at this moment and for the first time the oddest impression of studying him—she had only hugged him before, with sentiment and sense there had been no pondering; and he could have wished now she would straighten her head, her carriage of which had an effect on his nerves. It didn't matter that he believed her not really to intend this when she wound up with a repetition of her idea that they must have his portrait, that they must make sure of it before that first bloom of his expression, as she curiously called it, should have died down; a particular need of his own came to a head under her scrutiny quite as much as if he feared probing. "I'm an honest man, I'm an honest man!"—he said it twice over, strongly and simply, conscious of a sudden that he enormously wanted to, wanted to with an inward sharpness of which he had not yet felt the touch. It was a pressure from within that thus spoke, a pressure quite other than the driving force that had carried him so far and that he had known but by its effects, so rapidly multiplied, and somehow as dissociated from their starting-point or first producing cause as if that origin had been a spring pressed in somebody else. It was in himself, deep down somewhere, that his motion of protest had begun, and it really eased him to give it repeated voice—even if when he had made the point, that of his honesty, four times over, he had come rather to resemble the lady in the play of whom it was remarked there that she protested too much. He felt himself verily colour with his emphasis, and that was not at once corrected by his having to face the question straightway put by Perry, who on his side repeated the word once more. "'Honest'? Pray who in the world, here, cousin, has rudely said you're not?"—*that* was what he should have had in consequence decently to answer weren›t it that his wish to clear himself *to* himself helped him to laugh, with whatever small flurry, at the challenge.

"It isn't your rudeness, it's your extravagant flattery, you dear people, that makes me want to warn you that you may find me, on seeing more of me, less possessed of every virtue than you're so good as to insist." He looked with his becoming blush from one of them to the other—becoming we call it because his act of difficulty and thereby of caution appeared to provoke in each of the women after all but a new, quite a brighter and fresher shade of interest. Were they going to like him uncertain better still than they had liked him certain, and if so to what should he look, besmothered as that must surely make him feel, for the comfort of knowing where he was for himself? Where he was for Molly, and by the same token for her mother, was told him by this pleasure they took in seeing how he had found, to his slight embarrassment, that there was something to explain. That it was that seemed to set him off in their eyes, which were so agreeably, if so oddly, affected by almost any trustful touch of nature or unexpectedness of truth in him. If he had hoped to please by intention, so he might perhaps have liked even better to please in spite of himself; notwithstanding which this last liability did to a degree contribute ease, or even, it might be, rather compromise dignity. He might for all the world have been *growing*, growing hard, growing fast; it had begun with the minute of his entering the house, and especially that room—so that without knowing what at such a rate one might really grow *to*, one should not yield to the imputation of being finally measured. There was a singular space of time during which, while this consideration on the part of the two women so approved him, approved him verily as against himself, approved him almost as if their soft hands had stroked him for their pleasure, there hovered before him the wonder of what they would have done had he been ugly, what they would in fact do should he become so, in any manner or form—this idea of his full free range suddenly indulging in a glance at that mode of reaction. What it all represented was doubtless but his need to express himself over the felt shock of his ignorance, since if it amounted to a shock the last way to treat it was to pretend he didn't mind it. He minded it, he found, very much, and if he couldn't pretend to himself he wouldn't pretend to the ladies, however they might want him confused for the enjoyment of smoothing it away. "You have then another daughter whom I hear of for the first time?" he asked of Mrs. Midmore—and indeed wellnigh in the tone of defying her to smooth that.

"I'm not in the least ashamed of her or aware of having at any time tried to conceal her existence!" his hostess said with spirit, yet with no show of resentment. "And I don't see really what it signifies if you have simply forgotten her yourself."

Ralph lifted a pair of finger-tips and, with thoughtful eyes on her, applied them for a moment—in no mere humorous fashion withal—as to a helpful rubbing of his head. There *was* something he so wished to make sure of. «No, I don›t think I forget. I remember—when once I know. If I don›t remember I haven›t known. So there it is,» he said for himself even more than for his relatives. «Somehow it does signify!»—after which, however, he threw the matter off with a laugh. "Better late than never, at any rate."

"I'm glad you grant us that," Mrs. Midmore returned, "for you mustn't have the appearance, you know, of wanting to cut us down. We're not after all such a big handful."

He gave a pacifying stroke to his disturbed crop. "No, I mustn't have any appearance that doesn't fit my understanding. But suppose I should understand," he put to her the next instant, "something or other that doesn't fit my appearance?"

"Lord, mother," Molly laughed out on this, "what on earth does the clever creature mean?"

Mrs. Midmore looked at him harder, as if she herself would have liked to know, but Perry had intervened before she could make that remark, addressing his observation, however, to herself. "I'll be hanged if I see how, if he didn't hear of sweet Nan, he could have learnt so much about the rest of us."

"Mercy, brother, what a stupid speech!" Molly impatiently exclaimed. "Does it depend so on sweet Nan that anyone should take an interest——?" She went on to her brother, but looking with this, in her rich way, at their kinsman and giving that gentleman thus any number of her frankest reminders. "How was he not to take in the news that letters asked for and that letters gave?—and how at all events, for my part, am I not to be quite content that he makes no stranger of me?"

"Yes, my dear," Ralph at once declared, "it certainly can't be said that I've made any stranger of you!" He took her reminders and gave her back for them proportionate vows—in spite of which what she seemed most to have passed on to him was the name she herself had taken from her brother. Thus it was that, incongruously enough, it broke from his lips too. "'Sweet Nan, sweet Nan!'—how could a fellow *not* be taken by a thing as charming as that? Sweet Nan, sweet Nan!"—he obeyed the oddest impulse to say it over and over. With which then, none the less, as if for avoidance of his turning silly, he addressed to his companion such a vague extenuating smile as he knew he would have taken, had it been addressed to himself, for a positive grin of aggravation.

"If you make so much of it as that," Miss Midmore amiably replied, "I shall have to think you love it better than what you might call *me*."

"Call you? Why, I'll call you anything you like. Miss!" he laughed—but still too much, as he felt, in the sense of his vagueness.

"Oh upon my word," she tossed up her head to say, "if you can't think yourself of what I should like I'm not the girl to hunt it up for you."

"What do you say to 'jolly Molly'?" her brother, on this, took leave to ask, putting the question to Ralph with an unexpected friendly candour. "If you had heard her named that way wouldn't it have made you want to know her? But perhaps it was the way, and that it was so you were taken captive. Of course I don't know, in spite of what they say," he went on, "what has shaken us so together."

"It must have been that he had heard of you as merry Perry!" the girl at once retorted; upon which Mrs. Midmore as promptly remarked that she had never in her life listened to so much nonsense.

"One would really think," she continued to Ralph, "that such things as letters had never passed between us, and that it's a mistake or a mystery that Molly herself, from a year ago, wrote to you under my approval."

"He wrote to me under my own," Molly said, while her bold eyes, all provoking indulgence, suggested to him again in that connection more matters than any he immediately grasped. But he felt he must try to grasp, having somehow got so ridiculously off and away. Of course he would have written to her, of course he *must* and with the lapse of another moment he had expressed this for his relief—making the point to extravagance in fact, in order to make it at all.

"I wrote you three to your one, you know—which I dare say *you* will have noticed,» he observed to her mother, «since I hope she was always pleased enough.»

"I grant you, cousin," Perry interposed, "that there has gone on here for months past such a sight of writing and reading as would have done credit to a lawyer's office. I congratulate you and congratulate *them* on what it seems to have meant.» He had spoken in franker accommodation than had yet come from him, and now walked away to the window, where, looking out, he drew a deep breath again; Ralph remaining struck with his odd alternations, those, as who should say, of a man who could lose his ease and fail of his balance and then once more recover them—which was in fact very much what was happening to our friend himself.

"I suppose you've kept my letters, every one of which I remember, as I've kept yours," Molly resumed in her great gaiety—"so that I can bring them down to you tied up with pink ribbons, and then, if we compare, we'll see who wrote oftenest; though of course I quite allow," she smiled, "who wrote best."

Ralph met afresh on this one of his needs to consider. "You have 'em tied up with pink ribbon?"

"You mean," Molly asked "that you've tied up mine with blue? Or that you've tied up mother's with black?"

He was conscious, once more, that the truth of this would come to him—but meanwhile, just for the instant, he wondered and waited. "You've really got mine to show me?"

"In return for your showing me mine; which—look at him, look at him!" she said to her mother—"I don't half believe you've kept."

He was obliged to hang fire but a moment longer—it was like that question of her portrait in his pocket. He hadn't been sure of that, but the miniature was nevertheless there. Her letters weren't secreted about his person of course, but where would they be else than at the bottom of that box at his inn? "If you can prove one of them missing," he was thus in twenty seconds ready to answer, "I'll chew the rest of 'em up and swallow 'em, red tape and all."

"Have you tied mine with red tape?" Mrs. Midmore asked in full amusement.

The pleasure of being certain when he could be certain was, he rejoiced to note, as great to him as ever. "We don't deal in that article as much in America, no doubt, as you do here, but one always takes it, you know, for binding—and if I'm bound with pink ribbon," he said to Molly, "I'll have you understand that *you're* tied, my dear, as the lawyers tie up deeds and contracts. So that›s the way,» he laughed, «I hold you to your bargain.» With which indeed, however, he had but to hear the elder lady enrich the air with her assurance that their bargain was the best witnessed as well as the fairest she had ever had to do with, in order to feel anew that pinch of conscience, as he could only have called it, which he had a few minutes before too insufficiently soothed. He might really have been telling lies within these later instants—by the measure, that is, of his recurrent wish to establish his innocence of the other recognition. His need in this connection withal was to be clearest to Mrs. Midmore. "Ten times on the voyage did I read them all over, and in fact if she dares to doubt of it I'll repeat every word of 'em before you and her brother—which is a threat, my love, that I think will keep you quiet," he gaily continued to the girl herself. And he had on it an extraordinary further inspiration—so far as one such was more extraordinary than another, and so far as what was now before him, for instance, was more so than that quick vividness, just recorded, of his sense, his positive exact vision, of the red-taped packets in the portmanteau. "I have them by heart with the funny spelling and all; and if our company only hear, without seeing, your sweetest passages, my dear, they won't know, they won't know——!"

"That I did once write 'affection' with one 'f', you mean?" Molly broke in with so little resentment as to convert into light banter on his part a stretch of allusion which he had risked with a slight fear of excess. "You'll find also when you look again that I once spelled 'frightful' *ite*—I remembered it after my letter had gone. And I remember something else too—which, however, I'll not confess to before them."

"You confess so charmingly," Ralph returned, "that it only makes me love you the more"—for indeed it really touched him that she didn't protest with blushes or other missish arts, but showed herself, as he might have said, splendidly shameless. This after a fashion drew them closer still—for what was it but the success of his pleasantry? and it struck him that she had at no moment yet "told" for so frankly handsome as in seeming thus to invite him but to come on with what humour he would. This allowed him once more all the taste of finding himself right—so right that, for the matter of her "friteful", he knew as well, which meant he remembered, that she had added an 'l' at the end, which she always did in like case. Of this droll grace he now reminded her, to the further consecration of the brave intimacy playing between them; the freedom of which reached a climax, however, in his being able to convict her at once of the peculiar lapse that she admitted without naming it. There were moments, light as air, at which he proceeded by spasms of exhilaration—renewals, that is, of his sense of the sudden, the happy, the far jump to the point of vantage that just offered room, and no more, for the tips of his toes, thereby making it a miracle that, besides exactly alighting, he should afterwards balance himself too in such pride, the pride well-nigh of the poet's herald Mercury on his heaven-kissing hill. There it was before him, Molly's own finest flight, toward the lower right-hand corner of one of her loosest pages. "Your guilty secret is that of the 'goast' at some haunted house where you had paid a visit—unless it was but a case of a plural gone wrong and a house really haunted with goats!"

She met him with the freshest interest over this, and it was extraordinary how nothing could more have expressed to him what a dear girl, in fact what a very fine young woman, she was; half the charm consisting moreover in the oddity that while she used, pen in hand, wrong letters galore, her lips, the loveliest in all the world, gave them to the ear in the fairest and rightest fusion, and testified to an education that would have had nothing to gain, one seemed to see, from better terms with her inkpot. It was much as if he had known in New York young women of a common literacy enough who at the same time carried no further the effect of breeding. His English cousin meanwhile denied, at any rate, the last aberration imputed to her—it wasn't a bit, she declared, her actual mistake, which latter, though really a worse one, he thereby showed he hadn't remarked.

He laughed out his desire to know what could be really finer than the flower he had culled, and was ready to prove to her that he had other flowers too by presenting her at her convenience the entire nosegay. The spirit of this contention on both sides would have continued, no doubt, to raise the pitch of pleasure hadn't Perry, turning round from his window as if to stare at a pair of comedians in a play, intervened in a manner that spoke again of the notable growth of his wit.

"As I think you've never in your life written to me in any absence," he said to his sister, "of course I can't answer for your way with it, especially as one has heard that love-letters are always distracted, and I wouldn't give a rap myself for one that wasn't"—of which last he rather solemnly notified Ralph. "My sister Nan," he further informed him, "isn't a girl to lose her head even when she loses her heart; there's never a word out in anything *she* writes, and whenever I›m away from her she does me the kindness.»

"Pray how can *you* judge of her style,» Molly asked in derision, «when you told me but the other day you'd bring me a specimen of your own to look over and then didn't?—which I think must have been because on your intending the first letter of your life you found the feat was beyond you. It was to have been to a lady, didn't I understand?—and you'll have lost your head, I suppose, even more than your heart, and were afraid of showing for more distracted than need have been."

Perry Midmore, under this retort, only looked at the girl as if her humour, keen though it might have been, already found his thought, drawn off; so that, unexpectedly to Ralph, his defence was but after an instant to ignore her and make, as with a decenter interest, an appeal to their guest. "I should like to show *you*, sir, how Nan can acquit herself, though I'm sure of course that you understand our exchange of compliments. We bandy words in sport and among ourselves, but don't take 'em, you may well suppose, from any one else. I quite agree with my mother," he further remarked, "that we're bound to take you for a man of the greatest taste."

Ralph had already noted in him that his eyes, which seemed to wish for some restless reason to keep clear of those of his announced brother-in-law, might at the same time have been resisting with difficulty some possibly better cause for not appearing to avoid them. He almost caught himself in the act of wondering after another moment whether this member of the family were not appointed to interest him more by a round-about course than the others by the directness which matched his own and which would perhaps give his own, after all, comparatively little to do. That flight of fancy couldn't but spring from the inference, now lively, that Perry was now practising the art of the straight look very much as he might have practised that of balancing his stick on his chin. Again with this, however, the difficulty recurred: wanting himself, and wanting much, to encourage the freedom, he yet troubled it by the look returned as a sign of that. Should he have, he asked himself, to shut his eyes so that his cousin might keep *his* open upon him? «Take me in, take me in, and see how little it will hurt you,» he felt he should have liked to say; but what came back was that just the intention of it defeated somehow as by excess of meaning the act of reassurance. What the devil could have been at stake, he seemed to see the poor man wonder, when one of the scales, to drop enough, demanded such a weight as that? All the while, none the less, Perry's success in facing him did go on. The great thing, Ralph therefore judged, was for them to miss no breath of real communication that either might feel he could draw. If either wanted practice here it was, and by way of proving this wouldn't he himself, our friend reflected, do just the right thing in playing a little with that question of the family tone? "Yes," he smiled at his kinsman, though signifying that he made the point scarce less for the ladies too, "yes, your way with each other is the pleasantest possible; but all the same, you know, I somehow feel mixed with it the presence of stronger passions and—what shall I impute to you?—fiercer characters than I've been used to in my rather heavy and puritanical part of the world."

"Good Lord, you don't mean to say you're a Puritan!" Mrs. Midmore quickly exclaimed, in the noblest horror.

"I guess we're all Puritans over there as compared to you," Ralph had no difficulty whatever in deciding at once to reply. "You're all high-coloured and splendidly of this world." He found a pleasure in saying it out, as he had been feeling it so from the first; besides which it was the remark of broadest application that he had yet permitted himself, and there was a degree of relief in that. This not least, either, on his seeing how it stirred Mrs. Midmore up, for nothing could be clearer than that whenever stirred up she would affect him at her grandest.

"Do you mean I don't believe in another world than this?" she asked, "when, as indeed as good a churchwoman as there is in England, I never miss a proper occasion of declaring it!"

"Well, we're Church folk too in New York, thank God," Ralph said, "but we've scarcely a church that you'd know from a conventicle, and don't you see how even in this elegant talk with yourselves I can scarce keep down my own snuffle?"

"It's you, I'm sure, cousin, who give our conversation its greatest elegance," Mrs. Midmore returned, "and I can't fancy what you mean by our high colour——!"

"Any more than I do"—Molly took the word straight from her—"by his calling us fierce, forsooth, or talking of himself as pale; when he has as fine a brown skin as one would wish to see if one likes brown men; which, however, I never dreamed I should, sir!" she wound up as boldly as ever. "I shouldn't have supposed we were fiercer than a country still containing so many blacks and savages," she as lightly remarked, "and, for our passions, I don't hesitate to say, need I, mother and brother? that I but live to control mine. What in life is our religion for," she inquired of Ralph with the same ready wit, "what is it for but just to teach us to do that?" He took her in afresh as she so put the case, but could pay her the frankest tribute and still return with a laugh: "Of course it's for that, and all I mean is that you strike me as kneeling to your Maker very much as you curtsey to your king—doing it too, to judge by the splendid service I attended at Plymouth after landing, among as many feathers and frills as ever would deck you out at court." There were moments when he so liked the way they listened to him as if his cleverness was beyond their custom that, this impression just now renewing itself, he could only go on. "Our feathers in America, you know, serve for the blacks, who bristle with them from head to foot like so many porcupines when they want to fight us; but," he broke off in friendly amusement at their reception of this, "there isn't a bravery you flaunt or a passion you succeed in smothering that I don't perfectly rejoice in and bless you for. I like you just as you are, and wouldn't have you or have anything a bit different," he sociably declared; "yes, yes, I'm more pleased with what I find you than ever I've been with anything in my life, and not least pleased with my cousin Perry," he resolutely pushed on; "even though he *will* look as if he doesn›t know what to make of me and wouldn't trust me a step nearer to him—or is it, still more than that, a step further than you can keep your eye on me, cousin?"

He put that question, but neither abating nor enlarging his distance; it was one of the moments of his holding them under the spell of his growing brilliancy, as he might for all the world have imagined—too much under it to move an eyelid for the time, and yet also with the betrayed impulse to exchange a wink, vulgarly so to call it, between themselves; the very impulse, all of sharpened comfort surely, to show each other *where* they felt together, which he had already more than once caught in the act of profiting by its quick opportunity. Not their impulse, however, and not any play of comment that should attest his success with them, was most matter for thought with him now; but exactly his himself so wishing to cry out that he was pleased, to say again and yet again that he liked what was before him, so that there might be no mistake about it for his own nerves. His nerves, happily and helpfully active from the first, had been in just that proportion a pleasure to themselves—so that up to the moment of his first hearing of sweet Nan, whom he was now so oddly unable to figure save as very peculiarly one with this term of allusion to her, which might *all* have been, as they said in Boston, her «given» name, up to that moment his sail had done nothing but swell in the breeze. Why the mere hint of *more* sweetness still than the already looked for and the already grasped should have suddenly caused the breeze to drop and the sail to indulge in its first, its single flap, was not so much his concern as to arrest the possibility of any like further little waste of force. It was glorious so to vibrate, but to do it you needed your force—in fact all there was of it; so that to spend even one throb of it on any mystery of a particular muffled point or fact was at the best a loose form of contribution. So played the instinct to make surer still what was sure; yes, such a truth, for instance, as the perfect practicability of Perry even, once he should be *really* reduced to matter of splendid sport. For didn›t it *all* keep becoming again splendid sport?—that is if he left out the question of sweet Nan, which seemed something different and possibly either of a lower sort of interest or of none at all; unless indeed possibly of a yet greater.

The pitch therefore was at all events that there was no hint of a doubt as to the clear taste of his feast while it thus continued to be served, as well as that the right expression could only consist accordingly of the loudest smack of his lips. The company then, after the fashion we have noted, admired him at this exercise, and his sense of rich free words on Mrs. Midmore's and Molly's part, to the effect that their passing muster with him was perhaps nothing to gape at, had for its sequel a silent turn of Perry back to the window, though whether or no in more complete accommodation remained to be seen. He had at any rate been sufficiently beguiled by his guest's renewed overture of a moment previous not to wish to rebut at once any impression of this. Ralph consequently continued a minute longer to celebrate that idea of his success, as he could but treat himself to the crudity of calling it; while Mrs. Midmore, on her side, and with the breadth of her wisdom, recommended him never to overdo the act of humility, since in their world at least, however it might be in his native, you didn't get much more than what you were ready to fight for, and had always best set an example to people's opinion of you.

"Well," he answered to this, "if I like you, all three, for every mark you carry, every one of 'em without exception, as I again declare, so I want you to believe in me to the same tune, without my leaving in the dark a single side by which I may shine. I'll be as proud as you choose—look at me *now*," he went on, "and see if you can doubt of that; but I'll be hanged if you shan't love me for my modesty too, since otherwise you'll miss it when it comes to your giving your friends the right account of me. You'll want to be able to say enough to excuse you——!"

"To excuse us pray from what?" Mrs. Midmore sought to know at the very top of her grand air. "Understand, for goodness' sake, that we excuse ourselves here, in the civil way, but from things we haven't done, and that the things we have, the course once taken, the act performed or the need obeyed, we stick to, please, with nobody's leave whatever asked. I should like to see, sir," she wound up at this great elevation, "who you won't be good enough for if you're good enough for us!"

It was just the kind of thing he found he liked to draw from her, though Molly showed now such a peculiar play of consideration for him as made his own eyes while he replied signal back to her. "Oh I leave it to you, I leave it to you—you'll see, as soon as it becomes a question of my really flourishing, for my own opinion at least, how much I shall leave to you. I don't say," he added after this fashion to Molly as well, "that I mayn't do you credit and service as much as you do me, but I'm not flattering myself that Molly at the utmost will know *all* my reasons for delighting in her, or even guess the half of them.»

"I'm perhaps better at guessing than you think," the girl returned, "but I've never myself indeed wanted more reasons for anything than that my taste is my taste and my choice my choice and that I believe myself able to defend them."

"Ah you splendour!"—he radiantly took her up. But she had at once gone on.

"I hope there's nobody I shall praise you to for your being humble-minded, for I can't think of an acquaintance of ours with whom it would do you the least good even if you should need the benefit. Look after your own interests, as mamma says—and we'll look after ours and let other people look after their's; they seem mostly able to!" And then as the glow of the sentiment on which she so could practise was still there in his face it virtually invited, as he could feel, another turn of her hand. "If that was a compliment to us just now about the strength of the passions in us, is it your notion that a person's modesty should figure as one of them? It puts the question, you see, of whether one would be modestly passionate or passionately modest—and I don't mind telling you, if you need the information, which you'll have to take from *me.*"

"You give me wondrous choices," Ralph laughed, "but I hope I can get on with the information I've by this time gained. That is about *you*, about *you*," and he drew out his considering look at her—any further intention in which, however, Mrs. Midmore impatiently checked.

"If you can get on with the nonsense she talks you'll do more than I sometimes can; but I really think, you know," she added, "that you're teaching us a new language altogether and that in our own dull company we don't say half such odd things."

"It's perfectly true, mother"—and the girl kept it up at her friend; "he has made me say more of them in the last half hour, not to speak of doing 'em, the happy wretch, than in all my long life before!"

"Ah don't speak of any influence of mine," Ralph cried on as earnest a note as had yet sounded from him—"don't speak as if you didn't yourself put into my head all the wonder and the pleasure. The proportion in which I take these things from you is beyond any in which I can give others back. Do you see what I mean?"—and his earnestness appealed even to Perry, who had within a minute faced about again as for intelligence of what was said. Mrs. Midmore's appearance bore out in truth the hint that *her* intelligence had reached its term—a fact rendering perhaps more remarkable any fresh aspiration of her son›s. It was at the worst of immediate interest to Ralph that this worthy, with a positively amused look at him, at once showed signs.

"If Molly's modest at all," he maturely observed, "she makes the point, I judge, that she's passionately so; whatever that may mean, she's welcome to the comfort. But *I* make the point,» he said with increasing weight, «that my sister Nan, sweet Nan as you properly name her, fits on the other cap—the more becoming, as I understand it, to any young woman."

"Sweet Nan, he wants you to understand," Molly intervened on this, "is a shrinking flower of the field, whereas I'm no better than one of the bedraggled!"

"I see, I see"—our hero jumped to the vision: "you're the one infinitely talked about, as how shouldn't you be? But your sister has her virtue."

"Her virtue, Lord bless us," Mrs. Midmore took him up: "why I hope to heaven she has, with so little to speak of else; though she'll be glad, no doubt, cousin, to know that you answer for it!"

"Oh there are all kinds of virtue!" Ralph still laughed in his harmonising way—which his hostess, however, on that article, wouldn't have too much of.

"I never heard of but one kind, which is quite enough. Thank you for putting on us more!" And she wished to know of her son what possessed him to make such claims. "If we work you up so about the child," she inquired of Ralph as well, "how shall you not be disappointed?—let her have as she will for you the making of a brave little sister."

"Oh but I can imagine nothing better than a little sister to match the bravery of the rest of you, the brave little brother and the brave little bride, walking all three in the steps of the brave great mother—since you're so good, madam, as to become in some degree mine too. I'm sure," our young man declared, "that all Perry wants is to fit to our shy sister that other cap of

Molly's—which one is it, my dear?" he asked directly of this young woman; and then before she could say: "Oh yes, the pale passion of modesty, which you won't let *me* fall back on: for the want, I mean, of a better one among ourselves at home.»

"How do you know Nan's shy?" the girl demanded straight; "for it can't be as if you knew by being so yourself! Can't you understand," Molly pursued, "that the man of my taste *has* only to be as bold as a lion and to think of nothing less?»

"Well, I don't of course know that she's shy—that is I *didn't*; though I was guided so well by my apprehension of yourself. Yes"—and he looked about at them with the fairly musing gravity of this recognition—"I shouldn't much mind, you see, if I didn't fairly seem so to miss it!"

"Miss *what*, sir, in the name of goodness?" Molly asked with impatience; "when you pull a face as long as if you were missing your purse! You don't suspect us, I hope, of hugging you to rifle your pockets!"

He felt himself flush, and also, with his eyes on them again successively as to show them how he smiled, felt the probability of his looking silly. "I make too much of it, I know; but what I miss is my having been right; I mean, don't you see," and still foolishly he heard himself explain, "about—well, about what we were saying."

"Do you understand our clever cousin, mother dear, after all?" Molly wailed in a filial appeal.

Mrs. Midmore's own attention helped to point the doubt. "He mustn't be *too* terribly clever for us, certainly! We enjoy immensely your being so extraordinary; but I›m sure you›ll take it in good part if I remind you that there is a limit."

"Yes, of course there must be!" he quite seriously agreed.

"A limit, I mean"—she bridled a little—"to our poor old English wit."

"Oh that's another matter—and when you look at me in a certain way—even when Perry does," he declared, though he could have bitten his lip the next moment for his "even"—"I'm more afraid of it than I ever was of anything in my life. I took your reminder to be for the limit of our pleasure together; though why," he demanded of Molly, "should we fall to speech of that when the article itself has scarcely so much as begun? I do enjoy you—I do, I do!"—and he showed, almost with vehemence, that he meant it for them all. "It's for that very reason I should have liked to be wholly right. But there I am again!" he laughed—"I can't keep off that strangeness of my momentary lapse, for though it was short it was sharp. However——!" And he beamed in resolute relief upon brave Molly.

"You can't keep off my everlasting little sister—that's what you can't keep off!" her bravery answered, though rather as to put it as helpfully as possible to his comprehension than to make a circumstance of her pretending to a jealousy that might or that mightn't become her. She struck him at that instant as not a little puzzled, and he had already felt how moving, in a person of her force, an unexpected patience would easily be. He had even for this one of those rarest reaches of apprehension on which he had been living and soaring for the past hour and which represented the joy he had just reasseverated; impatience was surely one of her bright marks, but he saw that to live with her would be to find her often deny it in ways unforeseen and that thus seemed for the moment to show themselves as the most delightful things in nature.

"Well, but it isn't she, it's my own stupidity where I ought particularly not to have been stupid." He replied with the good-humour which he desired to feel so much more than anything else, and would have explained further but that she cut him straight off—he did of a truth, in spite of everything, keep giving her such opportunities.

"Is what's so dreadfully the matter with you, pray, that if you had known there were two of us I'm exactly the one you wouldn't have preferred?—so that you took me in other words only because supposing there was nobody better!"

"There *could* be nobody better, love!» he promptly enough laughed—and yet somehow felt it a little weak for the absurd intensity of the question; since the case *was* really that, more and more desirable as she grew with every point she made, it did inwardly and inexpugnably beset him that the fine possession of truth on which he had been acting wasn't then so very fine if it left a secret humiliation possible. There was a word on his tongue that would help indeed to preserve the secrecy; which was stayed, however, by a prior word of Mrs. Midmore's.

"Does the younger girl, in America, cousin, push in for an establishment before her elders are properly settled?" The question, uttered with all kind coolness, referred itself, as he felt, to the perfect proprieties, yet nothing had so placed the speaker in the light of the manners surrounding them, and he couldn't have told why it was unanswerable save by his going into more things, and perhaps even meaner things, than he then could care for. He wasn't, was he? pledged to Molly, or she to him, through her being offered in the order of the proprieties; but his kinswoman, in spite of this, could easily have convinced him that his not taking her point would be low. For what was the old order in which he found himself so triumphantly, even so pantingly, float but a grand order? and what his having at some moments to breathe so hard but the very attestation of his equal strength? It was when he breathed hardest, he again recognised, that his throbs meant most to him; and he perhaps hadn't been so little at a loss for anything as now for the right humour and the right look. "It's everywhere easier, I suppose, to find a wife than to find a husband, but marrying, as in all new countries, I take it, proceeds so fast that you'd scarce notice by watching among us, in any company, who comes in first. Those who do that here," he developed at this high level of urbanity, "do it doubtless by a longer stretch than we ever have to show; but how shall I tell you what I mean by there not being perhaps so many there to come in last—or such a difference even, for that matter, between last and first? I dare say you wouldn't at once know many of 'em apart."

These were still for his audience wondrous explanations—they plainly required among the three some art of following; though the three, it was to be added, combined at moments, rather oddly, an appearance, a positive hush, of blankness, with the signified sufficiency of their own usual names for things. "We're not accustomed to think here that the last are as good as the first," Mrs. Midmore said, "and if you want to see the differences there *can* be between them I flatter myself we shall have plenty to show you. You must let me tell you too," she went on, "that now that I know you I don't believe a word of their all dancing in America to such a tune as yours, and I believe it exactly least when you argue in such a pretty way for it."

This appeared so to express her daughter's feeling too that Molly borrowed at once the fortunate word. "And his being a bachelor in spite of it, what's his argument for *that*, I should like to know! If it's so easy to marry there, and nobody can keep out of it, somebody ought to have caught you before poor me—though I'm sure I'm much obliged to all of those who failed."

"Ah, my dear, none of 'em quite 'failed'" Ralph laughed.

"'Quite, quite'?"—she echoed his amusement. "A miss is as good as a mile, and a girl either gets a husband or doesn't. Unless you mean"—she kept it up—"that though single you're engaged: to some other sweet creature, or perhaps to a dozen, as well as to me." And then while he felt himself exceed his smile as she blazed on him with this, "I don't *hold* a man single who drags about twenty hearts: he's no better than Bluebeard himself—unless found out in time."

"Fortunately I'm found out in time then," Ralph again laughed—"that is in time to give you the key of the dreadful room and yet trust in spite of it to your courage—not to say to your regard."

"'Regard' is a fine word when you mean my foolish curiosity!" With which of a sudden she looked at him, he seemed to know, still harder and more intendingly than hitherto—to the effect in fact of his feeling more than ever how sufficiently he must meet it. That sufficiency, yes, took all his care—pulling on it there quite supremely; but there was notably always the luck that whereas such exchanges with her might have resulted for him most of all in the impression of something almost deadly in her force, what kept overriding them was the truth of her beaùty. If this last indeed was of itself a deadly force he could but oppose to it an accepted fate—for what turn of her head, of her hand or of her spirit wasn't somehow a flash of that treasure? How she knew as much herself too, and fairly bettered it by rejoicing in it! "If I stare you out of countenance—and I do, mother, don't I, if you'll look at him!—it's because I'm not ashamed of my curiosity, or of any other good reason for looking at you! I thank you for the key, as you call it," she laughed on, "and I'm sure I already see the poor things strung up in their dreadful row."

"You must really forgive her for a nasty torment," said Mrs. Midmore on this, and not a little as if she had seen that he *was* out of countenance. «I should think very ill of you if you had broken no heart—*I* had clean broken a dozen before I patched up my husband›s. After that, however, I assure you I kept my hands quite off; and if Molly will expect you to do as much now yourself, it's no more than you'll expect of her and that I give you my word for it I'll back you in. I should be ashamed of her as well, I don't mind saying, if nobody had been the worse for her—though of course one knows how much less a gentleman need be the worse than a female. It isn't to me at any rate that I ask you to confess," she nobly and brightly added.

"Well, I confess to *one!*" Ralph on this felt himself moved to break out. He had visitations, had been having them uninterruptedly and with a vengeance—looking for them, invoking them, enjoying them as they came; but there was one that took him by surprise and that in the oddest way sinned by excess. He hadn't three minutes before expected it, and as soon as he had spoken it seemed irrelevant. There it was none the less for himself, and at least, with his bravest ring, he could stick to it. "One, yes, one. I won't disown her. That is," he qualified, "I was myself greatly smitten, and seem to have let her know it. But I must have let her know it," he laughed, "in vain!"

"You 'seem to have'?" Miss Midmore echoed—"but you're not quite sure, any more than of how she treated you? It must have been one of your pale passions, as you call 'em, truly—so that even if her ghost does hover I shan't be afraid of so very thin a shade."

Our young man cast about as in some wonder of his own, meeting now but for a moment the eyes of none of them. "Yes, it's a thin shade—and melts away hiding its face, even while I look back at it."

"She may well hide her face," Mrs. Midmore improvingly cried, "if she was ever such a fool as not to have felt your worth. Still," Ralph's hostess went on with her fine air at its finest, "it's a comfort to know the worst of you—which seems to be no more than that you recover easily from disappointments."

Ralph faced her for this, his wonder again in his eyes—that wonder at himself which had on occasion, as appeared, a sharper play than any inspired by his friends. "I don't know about that—no! But as I'm not disappointed now, and am plainly not going to be," he at once added, "I don't see that the question matters. And when once I learn a thing I learn it—I do really make it my own," he added by an odd transition. "I had to learn—that was my point—about sweet Nan; but now that I have, but now that I know it's as if I had known always, or have at any rate lived down my surprise." He put that to them thus with earnest frankness and as if it might much relieve and interest them; and was moved with it in fact further to image their general dependence. "It's as if there were a few doors that don't yield to my push—though we've seen most of them fly open, haven't we? Those I mean have to be opened from within, as you've also seen." And again his point was made for his listening friends by that fine ingenuity which they either, to judge by something recurrent in their faces, couldn't sufficiently admire in him or couldn't sufficiently follow. "The case is that when once I am in the room it takes on quite the look of nature—at the end of almost no time." And then as with the quality of a certain hush in them beyond any of the several he had already had occasion to note his bringing about, he plunged deeper rather than shook himself free—dived to pick up, as who should say, just the right pearl of cheer. "I'm not speaking literally of this room—though it does strike me as extraordinarily beautiful. I've taken it all in—there isn't a spare cool grace in it that I don't admire." He waved at it all vaguely while they stared—yes, more than ever stared. What was he saying, what was he saying? he even inwardly questioned under the effect of that; which effect too, however, was that of his not caring so long as he cleared the matter for himself. "I mean a kind of idea of a room; so that catching the idea is what I call crossing the threshold. The thing is that when

I catch it I really hold it, don't you see? The thing is that when I know where I am all the rest falls together and I then defy any bewilderment. But I have to know where I am first. I did that perfectly the moment I came in here, the moment I came in there below. I defy you," he smiled and smiled to the three, "to prove on me any bewilderment—save that of course about sweet Nan, which we've all now got completely over." The pearl of cheer, held up between his fingers, threw out its light at them after the manner of pearls. "I've lived into *her* truth—yes, lived on into it, and all in a few minutes, shouldn›t you say, doing me that justice? So that now I'm ready for anything."

It was Perry who took this up first, though not till after an interval, curiously prolonged to Ralph's measure, during which that appearance for our friend of his companions' helpless failure of any sign of their reading into his solicitous speech an imputable sense, however off-hand the imputation, amounted practically to a rupture of relation with them and presented them to his vision, during a series of moments, wellnigh as an artful, a wonderful trio, some mechanic but consummate imitation of ancient life, staring through the vast plate of a museum. It was for all the world as if his own interpretation grew, under this breath of a crisis, exactly by the lapse of theirs, lasting long enough to suggest that his very care for them had somehow annihilated them, or had at least converted them to the *necessarily* void and soundless state. He could understand that they didn›t, and that this would have made them take him for mad, the chill and the dismay of which—felt for that matter by Ralph too—turned them to stone or wood or wax, or whatever it was they momentarily most resembled. The chill was a true felt drop of the temperature, the waft across them all of a mortal element, mortal at least to the others and menacing, should it have continued, to himself. That it couldn't possibly have continued, at such a portentous pitch, however, was the next instant standing out to sharpness in the fact of natural sound, sound borne up to them as from the cobbles of the Square and floating familiar life back to them. Perry's voice it was, positively, that had the warmth, and that was already, for the good of all of them, translating the suspense into terms. "Are you ready for Sir Cantopher?" he asked of Ralph with a pertinence which, as soon as thus attested, seemed to have picked up our young man's declaration with an overreaching hand. *There* was something they could rally to, particularly as a loud rubadubdub at the door had followed the report of arrested coach-wheels before it. «Ah, there the dear man is!" Mrs. Midmore at once recovered her faculty to say—even if all to the immediate effect of calling on Ralph first to search his own.

"Sir Cantopher, Sir Cantopher?" It was nature again for Ralph even if it was in its prime newness uncertainty. And it was uncertainty but just enough to prepare his glow of response. "Sir Cantopher Bland? Why, there's nothing I shall more prize than the honour of his acquaintance."

"He looks forward eagerly to the pleasure of yours," Mrs. Midmore remarked with clear assurance; so that Molly was the last to speak—which she did all to the tune again of her own high colour.

"I hope it won't interfere with your liking him, sir, that as you've been so taken with the fancy of my sister, he's taken worse still and from years and years ago."

"Oh he's in love with her? Yes surely, I know that—know it now," Ralph added.

"Of course you know it when I tell you, dear," the girl returned smiling, but with her eyes, it struck him, searching him as we have just noted his having had to search himself. He felt it as more of a watch of him in spite of his word than anything had yet been, and this he resented in proportion to his pride in the fine presence of mind he had so quickly recovered. So that made him positively go further, go in fact a length which was the longest he had used up to now.

"Ah I know more than you tell me, I know what I've *been* knowing. Of course he is in love with Nan,» he made out «almost as much in love with her as I›m with you. Only with the difference,» it came to him, "that his passion isn't returned——!"

"As I return yours is what you mean, dear?"—she took him straight up. And then when he had quickly pronounced this exactly what he meant, with a glance too at the fact that so much was evident, he had still to meet her asking how he could be so sure when they had been having it from him, and to the extent of his fairly complaining, that no information about her sister had ever reached him. The effect—he at once took this in—was of his being fairly cross-questioned, so that he should somehow be put to the proof of what he might say with the very entrance of the gentleman who would have already alighted below and perhaps be now on the stair. She really pushed it quite home. "You complained, you know, my dear, that we had left you in such ignorance."

"Ignorance of Nan, yes—only not ignorance of Sir Cantopher, at least as a ground of complaint. But I don't mind a bit, you see, what I didn't know before: that's all made up to me," he found himself pleading, "and I *want* so, don›t you understand? to be with you in everything.»

It was not unapparent to him meanwhile either that Mrs. Midmore, during this exchange, was momentarily mystified at her daughter's share in it, or that Perry, quite detached apparently from any question of a step toward their visitor, had witnessed for *his* attention by turning again to the window. But it was to himself directly that his hostess addressed a more confessedly puzzled expression than had yet comported for her with her dignity. «My child must sometimes seem to give you the absurdest notice of a temper!" And then after an instant to the girl: "Don't, you gipsy, make yourself out *more* of a romp than nature has done.» With which she appeared really, as the surer way, to appeal again to Ralph, who noted at the same time, however, that she might, by the betrayal of her eye, have caught some sense of her daughter's reason. "When everything's so right," she asked, "how can anything be wrong?"—and she had put no other question with so near an approach to a quaver.

"Do you think that to turn your head isn't what I most wish in the world?" were the only words, and splendidly spoken to her lover, with which Molly took up the remonstrance. "Mother herself knows that, just as I know how she wants it scarce less. But all the same, dear sir," she continued thus forcibly to reason, "I must put common sense between us for *your* sake even if I can do with fancy for my own. It isn›t a thing to quarrel about, even if anything *could* be,» she shiningly pursued, "but you must keep your head steady enough to satisfy me here. If you hadn't been aware of our friend's cross mistress, how could you be aware of our friend himself, who thinks of nobody else, and even talks of nobody, when he can get tired ears to listen?"

Ralph felt himself in the box, but also that never was a witness to have seen his embarrassment so enrich his interest. "Oh is she cross——?" The tone of the cry must have been comically candid, for it moved the ladies together to such a spasm of mirth that Perry, who wasn't amused, looked round to see why. Before which even, however, their kinsman had continued much to the same effect: "And he thinks and talks of nobody——?" Though with all gaiety, since they were gay, he corrected it a little for Perry. "Of course, of course—he does as he likes!"

Perry faced him on it. "He does indeed—and why in the world shouldn't he? It's the kind of gentleman he *is*."

This was really, for Perry, an explanation, and Ralph beamed acknowledgment. "It will be delightful to see the kind as you grow them here!"

"Ah nobody could be more civil," Mrs. Midmore interposed, "and very few, I assure you, cousin, are so clever and so keen. But surely, as he doesn't come up, you should wait on him below," she said to her son.

This worthy none the less didn't stir; he only stood looking at Ralph; with which, to the latter's surprise, he carried explanation further. "I don't say he's *my* man, mind you»—it was positively pacific. «And you can guess whether I›d be *his*, as my mother describes him—apart I mean from his liking Nan and our wishing to see her suited."

"Which she isn't of course," Ralph said, "if she doesn't like *him!*" It was as if Perry of a sudden had opened to him, and as if moreover, feeling this, he couldn't too cordially meet it. He met it most indeed by carrying his response on to Molly. "I see her as 'cross'—so far as 'sweet Nan' admits of that—because of her perhaps fearing that you want to overbear her. That is that you all together do, I mean—for I don't make it personal to yourself, dear!—and, as she holds out against you, treat her to the discipline of bread and water in a moated grange to see if it won't bring her round." The way to deal with his mistress, he more than ever felt, was to deal to extravagance—which was clearly at this moment so right that it seemed to invite him to pile it up. "If she'll have him you'll take her back, but if she won't, that is *till* she gives way, she›s reduced to her crust and her cell. Only,» he asked to the same effect, «how can Sir Cantopher himself suppose such rigours will serve him?"

"Here *is* Sir Cantopher himself, to satisfy you!» Mrs. Midmore cried—for the opened door now gave passage to the footman who had admitted Ralph and who announced the awaited friend. She called her welcome to this personage almost before he appeared. "You take your time, you pampered thing—when we've never so much wanted to see you!"

III

If the moments at which Ralph had felt the happy enlargement of his situation, during the past half-hour, had been much more numerous than those at which he was held of a sudden in a sort of constriction, he now knew within the minute that the elation of ease had caught him up high and higher. This came at once from the sight of the gentleman who entered to kiss Mrs. Midmore's hand before he did anything else, though indeed he gave Ralph a glance by the way, and of whom our young man at once conveniently noted that he performed the pretty act not at all as by prescription but somehow as by special inspiration, or even by the custom of oddity. He made a difference, the quickest—his arrival made it, and his look at Ralph and his fine good-morning to the others, before he had spoken a word but this last; the difference, that is, of replacing by their interest in his presence a certain self-consciousness on the part of each of the four into which their commerce of the last ten minutes had perhaps a trifle awkwardly tightened. And this verily, wasn't it? just by no more than the glance of his eye, a small sharp eye in a long narrow face, giving a sense as it did on the spot for Ralph's imagination to Mrs. Midmore's warrant of his keenness. Was it anything more than that he was intelligent?—though why if it wasn't could Ralph's heart leap up so without thereby implying that the others, the so agreeable others (for hadn't Perry turned agreeable too!) had beguiled him but with the common? However the question hovered but to drop, for there was no conceivable tribute to taste that his grand kinswoman didn't seem to render as she said to her new visitor: "I desire your acquaintance for our cousin Mr. Pendrel—a faraway cousin, but a near relation of another sort, as he is about to become my son-in-law."

"Do you settle such grand matters in the turn of a hand?—if, as I gather, Mr. Pendrel, whom I rejoice to see, has scarce had time to draw breath in your house!" Sir Cantopher addressed this to the others, but paying Ralph the compliment of it, as our young man felt, and letting him see that he might figure for unduly driven should he choose. It took, however, but this first vision of his fellow-visitor to put such a choice quite out of the question; the effect of this gentleman was so to make him throb again with the responsive curiosity that had carried him the whole length of his first initiation. That tide was once more full and strong, for here was a new relation, of the liveliest, which was already in the brief moment drawing him on and which in fact had in its different way as much force to that end, whatever the end might prove, as had been put forth for his original welcome by Molly herself. Molly had desired him, and Molly still did, as much as ever, he perfectly felt, all outer ruffles of accident notwithstanding, just as his own strongest pulse beat upon her for its satisfaction with a quickness undiminished; but the very face and air and note of the man before him, and who was as much taken with him, in the way of wonder, he could see, as he was himself taken, now multiplied at a stroke his relations with his actual world. Sir Cantopher's forehead was high and his chin long, without other fulness, as was also his nose; his mouth, with its thin tight edges and its inconsiderable size, repeated to the attention the fashion of his eyes and their drawn lids, which showed the sharpness of the pupil intermittently, much as the lips, opening too little, showed the gleam of scarce more than a couple of such teeth as would have announced on more liberal terms a proper array. Sir Cantopher's facial terms were precisely not liberal—in the sense, as we might have put it, that they made, in spite of resources close at hand, a hard bargain with expression; Ralph even noting for it at once that he had his aspect certainly, and that one took it somehow as a thing of high sufficiency, if not of beauty or symmetry, but that not less surely, should it continue to be denied larger play, it would have to do, unlike even the Greek theatric mask, both for tragedy and comedy. Would one ever, without other help, know which of the two he fixedly meant?—though doubtless he was meaning comedy now and moreover was, by some indescribable art and unsupported by a single direct grace, expressing a high degree of elegance and of consequence. It might be a small world in which he so much mattered, but there was exactly the charm, or at least the challenge—curiosity always predominant—that one might come quite to learn and to enjoy his conditions. His shoulders sloped, his stature but sufficed, and wasn't some slight deflection from the straight to be confessed to by his extraordinarily thin legs, in their understrapped buff pantaloons, a pretty match to a complete puce-coloured frock of the very finest smooth cloth, now left open to the bristle of frill and the ribboned dangle of watch-fob? The point most of all made by him at any rate was that of his being in his way, and the more remarkably as without her facilities, not less the fine gentleman than Mrs. Midmore was the fine lady.

"Oh our happy understanding was arrived at long ago!"—Ralph found himself liking to speak as if endless generations had prepared it. "You'll understand how with such a wind in my sails I couldn't be slow to get into port. And the kindness," he said, "with which I have been treated this hour——!" He left that to bridge all gaps while his face invited his relatives to see how for others still than themselves he put himself in their hands.

They saw it at once, they rallied, as he felt, altogether, and Sir Cantopher's presence crowned all their confidence without at all impairing his own. Ralph had been having from them this and that about him, but to see him there was to understand him as the supremely valid family friend, with certain of whose aspects liberties of remark might be taken behind his back, but with whose judgment and whose taste they would ever, and most particularly, wish their appearance as a family to consort. Our young man, with the divinatory gift that so unfailingly flared up in him under stress, was quickly mastering the truth that, for that matter, criticism of his friends would enjoy a range on this visitor's part which it could scarce hope to achieve in any conditions on Molly's or her mother's, affirm their claim to the luxury as they might. It was wonderful, it was already inspiring, that Sir Cantopher, by the mere action of a sign or two of the simplest, seemed to blow on the perceptive flame as if he had directly applied his breath. He recognised, he recognised—Ralph took that almost exultingly in for the quickening of interest it surely promised. What he recognised was that the American cousin appeared to justify himself to sight; which was perhaps no great showing, especially as an effect of but two or three glances—yet it offered that pilgrim an inviting extension, one he only asked to make the most of.

"I know how they've looked out for you, sir—and don't mind telling you that I've myself looked out *with* them; so that I perfectly conceive their present satisfaction. We›ve landed our prize—the expression seems peculiarly just, and you of course are assuring yourself with the last conviction that your own is at least equal to anything you could have imagined." Of these words Sir Cantopher delivered himself in a voice of such an odd high nasality as again threw Ralph back on the question of voices and caused him to note that he had never before heard a like tone applied with such confidence. It was with confidence and to the happiest effect that Mrs. Midmore applied hers, but hers was a charm and a rich comfort, whereas Sir Cantopher's excited surprise, or was exciting Ralph's at least, in proportion as it developed. There again accordingly was our friend learning at a leap, learning that here was a scene where the safe retention of properties and honours didn't in the least depend on a gentleman's either denying a single mark of his ease or attempting to please in violation of it. He himself had been acquainted, hadn't he? with the reign of the nasal, but when and where had it flourished to his ear as this gentleman, and doubtless quite unconsciously, made it flourish? People were supposed at home to enjoy in that particular an unresented license—which he had, however, never heard taken as he now heard it without its having somehow seemed to pull the speaker down. Sir Cantopher was up, up, up—yes, as he went on, up at the topmost note of his queer fine squeak, which was clearly not less an element of felt assurance in him than the most settled of his other titles. This didn't withal diminish the fact that if you had caught the sound the first time without sight of its source, you might have turned to expect some rather ancient lady, of the highest fashion indeed, but playing her part, presumably to her disadvantage, upon an organ cracked beyond repair.

It was furthermore of moment that not a shade of disadvantage, even while the impression was suddenest and sharpest, appeared attachable by Ralph's fancy to Sir Cantopher's similar exercise, for how could one in that case have been so moved more and more to advance in proportion as it was suggested that one was awaited? It took no great number of more words to represent to him that he was now in presence, and might ever so fortunately continue to be, of more cleverness even than his cousins had engaged for on behalf of their patron—his pulses telling him in this remarkable way that the finest parts of it would probably come out to him, and that, yes, positively, they were already wanting to come out. He, Ralph Pendrel, should enjoy them even were that ambiguity of the oral medium a condition involved. Mightn't he too grow with association prolific enough fairly to like the ambiguity?—even as it couldn't but be that the company Sir Cantopher kept had either to like it or, as the phrase might be, lump it. Ralph had really not to wait longer than this for the first glint of a truth that was soon to gather more force, the virtual perception that the only way not to find one's self rather afraid of such a companion might well be the device of getting and keeping so near him that his power to alarm should by positive human pressure be deprived of range and action. Not this calculation indeed do we impute to our partaker of impressions during the first stages of the relation that had begun so quickly to move him; it was quite enough that a surrender to it—though to *have* only just to surrender was a most extraordinary turn—looked for all the world like the door of a society, of knowledge, of pleasure in a rich sense in which he hadn't yet encountered pleasure, standing ajar before him and asking but for a push of his young hand.

"You'll understand, please, sir," Sir Cantopher had at any rate soon said, "that I'm here this morning to pay *you* in particular my respects and to offer you any service in my power. I›ve only to meet your eye, haven›t I? to judge that our manners and customs will be an open book to you almost at once, so far as a quick understanding is concerned; but there may be a page here and there that I can help you to turn over—even if your cousin Perry, who is also my good friend, may be a much better guide for you to the sights of the town, as they are called, let alone too most of the humours of the country. There are things Perry could show me, I'm sure, that I've never seen in my life—but that must be because he has never thought me worthy of 'em: isn't it, you great keeper of your own counsel?" the family friend asked again of the family hope, who now stood with his thumbs in his waistcoat armholes and his eyes anywhere but on Sir Cantopher's. He had no answer for the question addressed to him, which flowered out of the speaker's urbanity with a special effect for that vivacity of observation in our own young man of which Sir Cantopher, to his high credit, had lost so remarkably little time in making sure.

What even he, however, in spite of that sharpness, couldn't have guessed, and this by Ralph's private and immediate certainty, was what the latter was at these instants most thinking of: which was neither more nor less than that whereas their companions, not many minutes before, had visibly not known what to make of various odd matters drawn by the rare force of the situation from their kinsman's candour, so no felt want of ease whatever could possibly greet on the score of its ambiguity even the boldest push of this quite other and very much greater cleverness. Yes, very much greater, Ralph at once owned, for nothing yet had perhaps brushed his perception with such a wing as the absolute interest of that light on the fact that Sir Cantopher, with superior resources to *his* of every kind (if the facial were excepted, though perhaps indeed the facial but worked in their own way,) might irritate, might exasperate, might really, to put it at the worst, humiliate, his present auditors, but would never produce in them that odd consequence, recently noted, of their finding themselves disconcertedly at sea. Should Ralph again by any accident so leave them? He hoped not, he had somehow felt the warning, we know, as the chill of a misadventure. Still, amid the wondrous things that so positively promised to happen, that, even that, had its suspended possibility; which in fact cast a shadow just appreciably the larger and the darker by reason of this appearance that he was in danger of expressing least, to any practical end, just when desiring to express most, and that there was on the other hand nothing his fellow-guest might treat them to, for that gentleman's special amusement, that wouldn't be intelligible, and quite cruelly so if need be, exactly in proportion to the fine taste of it.

That was the point to which our adventurer reached out, the attraction of such fine taste as he had heard of, as he had dreamed of, as he knew existed in the world, without his having come even within remotest hail of it, but which he now by the mere act of a step or two might positively feel his hand touch. Of this he had for the instant so intent an awareness that the precious quantity in question and its curious master might, by the measure of the recognition, have seemed to supersede his appointed mistress and her bloom and her beauty as the main and original reading of his lesson and object of his aim. Wasn't he afterwards quite to allow to himself that he had during certain moments just then fairly invited the girl herself, so far as laughing toward her as if he desired it went, to be glad with him for his so liking what was thus promised them together, as might be—there having begun in him too, under the very sense we commemorate, who should have been able to say what instinct of the rightness of his making no sort of surrender to which he shouldn't be able to introduce her as well? Was he to pretend there, however, after but five minutes of their visitor's company, to be ready himself with services in any such particular?—services from which he might easily, if he didn't look out, borrow the air of an officious ass. It quickened everything, it somehow, with a kind of still and not absolutely harsh violence, jostled all things together, that she didn't, no, didn't at all glow responsive to this evidence that he could show eagerness, and eagerness so gapingly flagrant, for a cause with which her concern would be but what she chose to let it. How long had it been before he noted, and then almost with a start, that during the establishment of his good relation with their fine friend, which clearly was proceeding by Sir Cantopher's action still more than by his own, she hadn't so much as once taken visual account of that worthy's presence, had in fact turned an eye upon him as little as Perry himself was doing? This would have been perhaps made up by her leaving of her lover to grin demonstrative if she hadn't markedly appeared to fail of coming to his help in it. They didn't help people with Sir Cantopher, Perry and she; which fact might possibly be already a guiding influence, unless it was a mere mark of the momentary case. On the former supposition it involved more matters than required present attention, though throwing so much light on the latter as might spring from one's guessing—what one after all had by this time independently guessed!—that the girl wouldn't love without jealousy and that here was a juncture for her at which, through some occult cause, the sharp passion stood in front of the soft. Her brother's incalculable attitude had become under the shift of the general pressure just her brother's affair, but Ralph hadn't to wait to see how Molly's discrimination against his own extravagance of sociability corrected as much as he could possibly have wished that quick fancy in him of her having through the sudden strange stress of a short time before held off from him altogether. That had been an alarm, and this even at the very worst wasn't, for that she didn't hold off in ignoring the author of their actual complication, that she much rather held on, held as she had at no moment held, could only be the true sense of her manner. She had reasons, and what were they? for not caring that he should want to see so supremely much of what other people, and this one in particular should it come to that, could do for him. These reasons of course essentially counted, even while she kept the expression of them back, for a renewed assurance of all she felt she could herself do; a truth contributing not a little to our hero's sense of himself as more bedevilled at this moment perhaps than at any yet, ridden since he was by the wish to lose nothing that he could on any terms whatever grasp.

He faced at that moment, to all appearance, the signal inference that he had come out, as who should say, for nothing singly and solely, not even for bestowing his heart and plighting his troth; he had come out for the whole, the finest integrity of the thing—the insistence of which now flashed upon him with the hard cold light of a flourished steel blade. In that light the whole was promised and figured ever so much more by Sir Cantopher than by Molly and her mother and her brother—in whatever separate harmony these three should move or act together. He gave it out as they couldn't possibly give it, and as their attitude, in very truth—for wasn't there a telltale shade even in Mrs. Midmore's too?—showed they didn't so much as want to. Sir Cantopher cut across them as with the edge of his fineness, waving them back a little and keeping them in place by one free and practised hand while by the other he sketched a hundred like possibilities upon the stretched expanse of Ralph's vision, which might have been an artist's uppermost fair sheet. Absolutely he drew things, their companions turning away their heads (and poor Ralph needing indeed to keep his own,) in recognition that as they of course could flourish no such pencil, so might they not either prudently snatch it from him; it not being in every house, even of the best traditions, that such a master was content to perform—it having in fact been to all probability quite noted that all impatience of his time or disposition to finish worked infallibly against the challenger.

"Yes, I've collections, treasures, and all as pretty things of their kind as you can hope anywhere to see"—this, Ralph knew at the end of three minutes, was one of the points he had most promptly made, and had then dropped for some other, though only next to retouch it with a neatness of caprice, repeating it as in provision of interest for himself and at once adding that there was nothing he either so loved or so hated as to play showman—it all depended on the case. "I've things I'd as soon smash with a hammer as invite people to admire who haven't some struggling germ of a natural taste. I don't care a fig, you see, for what's called an acquired one, which is sure to have been begged or borrowed or stolen, sure not to have been grown. I don't know where you've picked up yours, sir," he was so good as to remark to Ralph with his sharpest civility—"for I can scarce imagine where you should. It must grow therefore in the soil of your mind—in fact, upon my word, I seem to see it grow in your very face while I speak to you: which is as becoming to you as possible and as promising, mayn't I say? for my own opportunity."

Sir Cantopher was struck—and Ralph was at once struck, as well, with his being so: he had put his fine finger so straight upon the spot where our young man's consciousness then most throbbed. Ralph *did*, as we know, grow many of his perceptions and possibilities from moment to moment and as they were wanted, but his sense of this had been up to that instant that he grew them deep down within and then served them up in the outer light only all prepared and garnished and denying their improvised state. Here was Sir Cantopher catching them crude, and as good as saying that he did; this at least with a confidence betrayed neither by Molly nor by Perry, symptoms of something like their friend's confounding note though they might have confusedly given. Ralph flushed under the effect of the liveliest observation he had had to meet, and we have already seen that flushing rather inevitably counted for him as blushing—and not the less either for the fact that when he blushed he took a perfect oddity of alarm, as if the telltale suffusion threatened him by a nasty little law of its own with loss or defeat or exposure; though exposure of what, in the name of goodness? These awarenesses during the moment or two, so pressed upon him and upon each other, that it was as if a recognition of what Sir Cantopher might mean fairly surged up, under the squeeze, from his conscience to his countenance, where it could thus only give such increased signs as made his critic the more frankly appreciate them.

"Don't you see what I mean and what a treat it is to seize in the fact such a candour of intelligence, a play of apprehension so full and yet so fresh?—as if born but three minutes ago and yet already stepping out as straight as you like!" So he pursued, the terrible man, inviting the others fairly to admire their kinsman's expression, embarrassed or no, and thereby, as we feel, making that expression almost glare about for a refuge, some dart to cover, some snatch of a tag of disguise, from its own very heat. "The next thing I shall cry!" Ralph reflected in a central gasp; but if he felt the tears rise he couldn't for his life rightly have apportioned the weight of shame in them against the joy of emotion just as emotion. The joy was for the very tribute itself of Sir Cantopher's advance upon him, whereas the shame was ever so much more vague, attaching as it did at the most to its being rather ridiculous to be so held up for transparent. *They* had seemed to him transparent, even with dim spots—he had been fairly on his way, hadn›t he? to reduce Sir Cantopher to it; so he panted a little, after his fashion, while the Midmores, and just exactly as through some blur of tears, affected him as rallying to their friend's invitation to see him in the light of that damning charm. He was what he was of course, and with the full right to be; but hadn't he half-seconds as of a push against dead walls, a sense of the dash at them in the dark?—so that they were attested as closely near without the fruit of it, since for one to call people reachable they had really to be penetrable. He said things—that is he was a little afterwards sure he *must* have said them, laughing, interrupting, deprecating, though he hoped not too literally—for he wouldn›t as yet have it that he didn›t on the whole and at the pinch carry almost any trouble off and see at the given moment more in the given matter than the others did. He was seeing even now surely more than Sir Cantopher was—which in fact however was exactly his complication, face to face as it placed him of a truth with his need to betray that he saw only what would save him; the idea of things that would lose him thus making its discriminations.

If he stood up, at any rate, the most pressing of his four patrons not only did that but struck him through it all as fairly spinning round with excess of balance—so at least poor Ralph felt on hearing it expressed as relevant that there was his handsome mistress, the finest young woman in England, for such were Sir Cantopher's terms, in whom, despite her thousand charms, no spark of the noble interest they referred to could possibly be kindled. "I don't complain of that," Sir Cantopher promptly added, "for she's a perfectly honest creature, with the very highest spirit and no shade of affectation, and in fact so rare a piece in herself that who can ask for more? You don't of course, sir, and I don't advise you to!"—Sir Cantopher's jerk of these last words was on an especially high note; "but there is a person in the family, if you don't happen to know it, from whom you may expect anything in life on the ground of taste; so long, of course I mean, as you don't propose yourself—as a mere brother-in-law to be—for the object of it. She has the most perfect understanding in the world," the speaker lucidly pursued, "in addition to being formed otherwise very sufficiently to please, and I'm such a fancier of every mode of the exquisite that I should delight in finding her young mind open to me if she didn't insist on keeping it perfectly closed. This is to show Mr. Pendrel"—he now addressed himself to Mrs. Midmore—"that I speak without prejudice, that I'm the most patient creature in the world, that I know when I'm beaten, and that I'm hoping for better luck!"

"Luck with sweet Nan is what I'm to understand?" Ralph had broken out, at the touch of this spring, before he could think twice, and very much in fact as if at last fairly dizzied by a succession of perspectives.

It seemed to add an instant's brightness to Sir Cantopher's hard little eyes, but Mrs. Midmore forestalled him. "Our cousin likes to name her so, though he complains of never having heard of her. You're making that up!" she said rather grandly to Ralph.

"Oh I seem to know all about her now," he more easily laughed, "and many of your names do strike me as differing from ours and as having a kind of charm." He was determined indeed to be easy at any cost. "I'm ever so taken with Sir Cantopher's—we've nothing at home like that," he instanced with a smile that covered the liberty taken, if liberty it should appear.

"Do you find it so much better than your own?" Molly inquired on this, in her outright way and as with a hint at impatience of many things.

"Ah, my dear, if mine's to be good enough for you I'm quite content with it—and it's indeed better than a great many we have. But I like Sir Cantopher more than I can perhaps make you understand"—our young man but desired to explain. It had at once, however, the effect of so moving to a queer small stridency of mirth the personage indicated, that a further remark was required. "I mean of course that we've no such honours, for the fine sound, and what shall I call it but the matching of the parts, of 'em?"

Whenever he explained—this perception grew—he produced a particular attention, the attention to which even Molly's impatiences yielded, and which had been most marked in the cold hush, consequent to all appearance on too much precipitation, vaguely scaring him just before his fellow-guest's arrival. It was the way indeed in which this fellow-guest now fixed him that made him grasp for an instant, as a sort of ban upon scares, the idea either of explaining a great deal more or of not explaining a mite. Yes, there was an extraordinary moment during which the four of them, Sir Cantopher included, affected him really as hanging on his choice—watching, that is, to see which course he would take. It was as if he did precipitate wonders, at a given juncture, just by some shade of a tone, a mere semiquaver, perhaps lighted too with a flicker of facial earnestness—though there was something all the while that he clearly couldn't help. It might, it must, have been the sense itself of spreading his wings, which would catch him up this way again and again, and which, when it came to that, he wouldn't have checked if he could, for how otherwise was he to surmount?—to surmount and surmount being exactly his affair, and success in it his inspiration, together with the fine truth that if the choice had to be between their puzzlement and his he'd be blest if he wouldn't risk theirs, since this there would doubtless after all be ways of surmounting, whereas he felt that mightn't be at all the case for his own. It had been repeated for him that each time he didn't flounder made somehow, almost immediately after, for the greater felicity of another time, and thus not to flounder at the actual point he was dealing with would be best assured by his right selection of the alternative they seemed so to wait for him to take.

He had taken it within ten seconds, had chosen: not again, no, not again would he explain the least mite; and they might make what they could of that—they would make more of it at the worst than they surely would make of its opposite. He kept up his gaiety for Sir Cantopher, hard as his innocence sought to temper it; which was what had just all but happened in his ridiculous identification of his sister-in-law to be. He mustn't use ridiculous terms—for now he could see that the name of his designation of her was so tainted, and what a trap had virtually been set him by Mr. Perry there, prodigiously instinctive Mr. Perry, who withal gave him the impression of a straighter and easier relation with Sir Cantopher than that enjoyed by the ladies of his house. This might have been but because they *were* ladies, any woman›s relation with almost any man proceeding, it was needless to reflect, by curves and crooks and hooks much more than by ruled line. Ralph, however that might be, felt himself face Sir Cantopher as with an accepted exposure to such penalties as would attach to leading him a bit of a dance by some turn that should possibly affect him as violent. Yes, he risked so affecting him, so far as the withholding of conciliatory graces of thought, those he had been scattering too many of, represented a danger. It would do most toward leaving him blankish, and being so left was probably always the accident with which Sir Cantopher had least to reckon. Ralph moreover wouldn't have been able to say, reducing it to that finest point, that if such a condition on the part of the patron of the Midmores might amount to a rather arid complication it would be after all the complication he should most mind. He was minding, that is he was averting, another much more than this in taking up what Sir Cantopher had been saying about his affianced bride. He did so under the conviction that leaving that personage to make the best of things would prove a less danger than leaving it to Molly—who, for that matter, waited upon his dealing with his difficulties, since as difficulties he so oddly chose to feel them, in a manner that almost put words into his mouth.

"I haven't the least idea where this young lady may be deficient for other people—I can only feel that I haven't a single flaw to pick either in her beauty, her mind, or her manners." Not only so much as that Ralph rejoiced to hear himself say, liking the sound of it still more, as ever, the moment he had uttered it, but he knew at once also how long he could have kept it up if he hadn't presently been stopped. "As far as ever she'll go in any sense I'll go with her all the way, and wherever she stops or wanders off I shall like her reasons for it, because they'll be hers—let alone that I'll wander with her too, believing that whatever turn we take together can only be for our happiness." The further words were perhaps a bit sententious, spoken that way before the others, but not enough, certainly not enough, could he publicly commit himself, with the effect of it again and still again that fresh and strange one of the motive, with all its rich force, constituted so much more after the fact than before it. He knew moreover, knew by something now as much represented in her face as if it had been a face painted on canvas just to express it, that he was acting as directly upon his mistress as if no word of it concerned their companions. That was his boon, to whatever result he did it, for he measured at this moment that he couldn't again have borne her having lost touch of him. It was indeed now as if he had read the words from her lips before she spoke them.

"I do like so waiting for what you say to such clever people—and then," she added with the greatest gravity, "not being in the least disappointed."

"My dear, my dear, how can a man as much in love as I am be disappointing?—I mean," Ralph laughed, "to the loved object herself?"

"I don't know. I'm sure, sir," Molly returned with a sort of solemnity, almost a sort of anxiety, that made her handsomer than any look she had yet worn. "If there were a way you'd be wise enough to find it; because, so far from my believing possible that you can fall short anywhere, as you have had to listen to so much about my doing, I see that the cleverness even of the most famous people will always find you ready, and don't care with whom it may ever be that I pass for a fool if I have wit enough for you as between ourselves. I like you as you are, sir. I like you as you are," Molly Midmore repeated.

"Now do you see sir, how fortune insists and insists on smiling on me?" Ralph asked of Sir Cantopher after he had done the most radiant justice to this declaration.

"I shall believe in you whatever you do—whatever, whatever!" the girl went on, her head very high, before their friend, whose curious hard connoisseurship had never strayed from Ralph's face, could reply to this appeal. And then it was that for the first time she rested her eyes on Sir Cantopher, whose own, however, they failed to divert. "You find out things about people, sir—though I really think them for the most part things for which one needn't mind your outcry. If I were to commit a crime, no matter what villainy, you wouldn't be the wiser, but you'd feel it at once in every bone, even if you were fifty miles away, should I knock over the dark blue jar that you gave my mother once upon a time and that's the pride of the breakfast-parlour at Drydown."

"And pray, Miss, wouldn't you call that a villainy?" Sir Cantopher said without taking other notice. "When I next go to Drydown," he continued to Ralph, "I shall count on finding it smashed——!"

"Oh sir, not if I interpose to save it!" Ralph again laughed, though keeping his eyes on the girl with a satisfaction that candidly grew. It was a queer necessity perhaps, this of his holding fast with one hand to a relation that he playfully ruffled with the other, even if not at all queerer, no doubt, than Sir Cantopher's own appearance of not being able to afford for an instant to remit his observation of our friend. It was at a triumph of the interesting that Ralph at this time thus assisted, and not a bit the less that the interest was imputed to himself. Was it in danger of disappearing if the sharpest of the pairs of eyes were for an instant removed from him? Ralph asked himself this with an odd recognition, it must be confessed, that what kept him up to expectation, if indeed it mightn't be what perhaps pretended to find him below it, really did, as an applied force, keep him up. "The worst you shall ever find out about Molly (though it's no more indeed than what she herself says) is that the blue pot at Drydown will stand as steady as I keep my balance here, for all your so watching me as if I were on the tight-rope; and, so far as she or I at least are concerned, will rule the scene there from the, from the—wherever the place is: wait a minute, wait!" He checked himself suddenly to plead for that indication, and yet too that they should let it come to him of itself; taking them all in now as if it glimmered and snapping with a fine impatience his thumb and his middle finger. "Don't tell me, don't tell me; I really all but see the thing and the very place: yes, a pot of about the size of—well, of that one there: only of a darker and richer blue. Bleu du Roy, don't you call it? and with something or other on the cabinet or wherever, the place where it 'lives', as we say, rather branching out on either side of it."

Ralph had been again caught up, as he had learnt to figure it: there had been nothing like it but his production, out of the breast-pocket of his coat, under Molly's inspiration, of that miniature portrait of herself which he hadn't then a minute before been so much as aware of his carrying about him and which had yet on his exhibition of it served all the purpose. How long ago had this been? He couldn't have said, such waves of experience had coursed through him since; but his present growth of confidence, recalling that other, seemed to be serving the purpose too, with a quick appeal to Mrs. Midmore, and a very impatient withal, determined by it on Sir Cantopher's part. "Have you really left that perfect piece with those clumsy candlesticks——?"

Ralph couldn't for a few instants have said what had happened: the effect was of his having by a word or two shaken his position, and that of his companions with it, quite as by seizing it in two strong hands and feeling it momentarily sway there. Mrs. Midmore, so far from replying to Sir Cantopher's challenge, just expressed that very sense—expressed it in a "What in the world is the matter with you, cousin?" which would doubtless have recalled to him that he positively glared with vision had the glare not, within the few seconds, caught a still bigger reflection from Perry. He was taken up for the instant with seeing, seeing what was half across the world, his world of these intense moments, at Drydown; and Perry, on whom in their searching way his eyes had thus lighted, seemed at that moment to be telling him things beyond belief. It wasn't even Molly now, still less was it Mrs. Midmore, so sharply spoken to and, in her indifference to it, with wonder only for *him*; it wasn't the prodigy of his right guess, so right, yes, clearly so right, about the posture of the prize at Drydown, attested thus by Sir Cantopher's recognition: it was the very horror in poor Perry's countenance, which conversed ever so straitly, as who should say, with the amused growth of confidence in his own and which once more lighted matters up for him while they were unexplained. Blest if he wasn't, therefore, before he knew it, in spite of lessons already learnt, mounted on the back of explanation—even though that winged horse whirled round as if to throw him; which it wouldn't do, however, so long as he held on to Perry's attention. Other things reached him but through his sense of that, above all Molly's comment on the question of how the blue pot was neighboured, guarded or whatever; this uttered, he knew, but without his caring, immediately after her mother's remark on his manner. He in fact scarce cared when his mistress pursued, as if it would account for almost anything:

"Most certainly she can't be accused of not heeding how things look: the place, when she's there, is at her mercy—she can keep her hands off nothing and spends her time in moving articles about to see how they look in other places. If Sir Cantopher means that I wouldn't touch a thing for the world I plead as guilty as he likes," the girl wound up while Ralph simply let the information float and fade—he had of a sudden got so beyond it.

Yes, launched on his demonstration he saw and saw—since it was his extraordinary communion with the affrighted Perry that helped him. Wasn't he seeing something that Perry himself had seen, or learning at least something that Perry knew, just by this compulsion of feeding, as it were, on his young kinsman's terror—for it had frankly to be taken for nothing less—and drawing to himself the sense of it? "Sweet Nan, poor sweet Nan!" he next found himself exclaiming, for what had happened was that he had with the strangest celerity read a particular knowledge into Perry's expression, and read into it as well the consciousness that he was giving it up, though to one's self only, not to the others, and that nothing so strange had in all his life befallen the hapless youth as to feel thus under the pressure of such an intelligence, which did definitely at last show the man betraying it for different, quite dreadfully different, from other men. Perry knew, unmistakeably, something intensely relevant to what they had been speaking of, and had known it all along, had had it in the place with him there from the moment, whenever that had been, of his first coming in; and now what was our friend not capable of, as a climax for this certainty, but just the final twist of appropriation which gave him use of the truth? Something had happened at Drydown between the head of the house and his younger sister, something of the day before, or of the day before that, which he would have made no great matter of hadn't the thought going on before him, to his scant participation, pulled it into view, into Ralph's, that is, as Ralph mutely showed him—but as Ralph also now at once next gave him reassurance for. Yes, yes again, there was something to save the girl at Drydown from, and he himself, with the flagrancy of his happy guess at the usual position there of Sir Cantopher's grand gift, had just grazed the treachery of publishing it. To have apprehended the accident, to have caught Perry catching him aware of it, like that, from one moment to the other, was by the same stroke to feel himself close his bodily eyes to it, ever so tight, and with more intention, for the three seconds, than in any act of all his life; this too in the midst of their mutual glare and, by what he could tell, after Sir Cantopher's attention, as well as that of the two women, was back upon the queer proceeding, which Molly's indeed had not quitted.

The duration of the exchange was assuredly to have been measured but in seconds, though in no such number of them had so much happened up to now, by Ralph's private measure, which indeed had considerably grown; only he couldn't not keep looking at Perry—wish as he might to explain, to go on explaining, for the benefit of the others, whose three pair of eyes treated him with anxiety, with admiration, or to the effect again of the sinister estrangement, whichever of these things it might be. The great reality was that his words, as they came, had to mean most to Perry, and could only come thus also by the help of his horror. That horror, by the end of a couple of moments, was what he was afraid of for the others still more than of his own queer visionary pull-up, his invitation to them to see him in presence of the Drydown sideboard, or whatever the ambiguous object, and then see him, in the very act, both turn his back upon it and try to scatter gold-dust round his revulsion.

"I'm not a prophet or a soothsayer, and still less a charlatan, and don't pretend to the gift of second sight—I only confess to have cultivated my imagination, as one has to in a country where there is nothing to take that trouble off one's hands. Therefore perhaps it is that things glimmer upon me at moments from a distance, so that I find myself in the act of catching them, but am liable to lose them again, and to feel nervous, as if I had made a fool of myself, when an honest man like my cousin Perry looks at me as if he thought me a little mad. I'm *not* mad, cousin Perry—I›m only a mite bewildered by the way I seem to affect you, since it might be catching for your mother and Molly and Sir Cantopher if I didn›t convince you that I don›t on the whole confess myself anything worse than rather a free talker."

"I like your free talk—I like it, I like it!" Molly broke in at this. "I wouldn't have it a bit different, though we have certainly never heard anything like it in all our lives. I'm not afraid of you now," the girl continued, "or else I'm no more so than I want to be—for I think I told you a while ago that I should miss your not sometimes putting me in fear. If you're doing that now—and I see you *are* doing it to Perry, whom I declare I›m sorry for!—I›m enjoying it still more than I could have hoped, and wishing I could only have some of my friends about me to see my pride, which means perhaps to see what *they* would make of you for a grand match. You›ll understand that I›m in the greatest possible hurry to show you off,» Miss Midmore wound up.

"Ah but I don't engage to perform by appointment," Ralph laughed—"at least in the sense of making our friends uneasy."

He rejoiced in Molly's reassurances, even if he couldn't yet let go of Perry either to acknowledge them properly or to be clear again as to the particular shade now of Sir Cantopher's curiosity. He somehow felt Sir Cantopher suspended, almost dangling in air, but ready to alight on one or the other side of a line that Ralph had himself the sense of actually tracing. As for Mrs. Midmore, it was as if she had just sunk down somehow or somewhere, looking very handsome on every contingency, but vague, certainly vague at present, and positively rather white. These things he took in while still resolute that he couldn't drop Perry till Perry had turned to safety for him or otherwise than by mere limpness. There was always the obvious chance that almost any far range of wit, which he never could have beheld such a stretch of as just now, would stir him to something of the same suspicion as a case of proved dementia. Moreover the young man was during these instants really plastic: he didn't want to back away—he but wanted again (and it recalled what he had seemed to want just after their making acquaintance) to have a perch held out to him across the fall-away of familiar ground, long enough to be grasped without his moving. "I do guess I figure rightly the features of Drydown," Ralph said, "and seem to see them, in perfect order, absolutely perfect order, thanks to you, sir, and the earnest young lady there, await my paying them a visit—which, however, you're to understand I shall only pay in your company, as master of the house and my proper first, introducer."

Molly had been herself launched by her speech of a moment before and her voice, as she did renewed justice to the pitch of her preference, fairly betrayed to Ralph's ear how finely she was agitated. "If you mean that to signify that you'd like to start for the country at once on a visit to my sister, I give you leave with all my heart to wait upon her there until you're tired of her. Because, you see, if I grant that you torment me by pretending you're already, after so little of me, tired of myself (of which, however, I don't believe a word!) the least I could do would be to torment you in return by the air of indifference under outrage. Of course, really, we're neither of us pretending, and you've more for all of us to be pleased with than we as yet understand. In that confidence of my own I think I should wait for you to come back to me from even further away than the breakfast-parlour at Drydown. You're to understand, please, that nothing you can do—so far as I rightly conceive what a gentleman may!—will break my confidence down."

"It's a poor reply to those beautiful things, isn't it, Perry? to say, if I haven't by now convinced her, that I'm not a gadabout, and that if your friends are so good as to want to see me it's they who have only to wait upon me here—it's a poor reply," Ralph went on, "but it must serve till I have it from yourself that you take me for accommodating and believe that I shall make you like me if you'll only help me a little to do it. Haven't I already as good as said to you that I'll do for you anything in life that you may be kind enough to mention, from the moment it's the least in my power? There it is, and I think you do already see that I absolutely want but to oblige you"—with which Ralph hung fire an instant as to drive it in by his very pleasantest intelligence, and then went on—"*am* in fact obliging you, *have* supremely obliged you. Good, good—and steady, steady:" he took it up in triumph, turning with it now to the others and inwardly sustained in his free attitude of inviting them to witness something that he didn't much care at that moment whether they understood or not, so long as he overrode them by a blinding assumption. It would be extraordinary to blind Sir Cantopher, but under that inward pressure he was ready to risk almost anything for it, as he had risked everything successfully, hadn't he? for the bedazement, the renewed conquest, or whatever he might call it, of Molly, of his action on whose nerves and senses and own pride of conquest he felt with each instant more certain. He smiled at them all again, carrying it off, carrying them on, and still but wanting Perry to take in that he impressed them. Molly in fact left her brother in as little doubt of that as if she had understood more than was supposable of the remarkable exchange, just concluded on his part, with their kinsman.

"You see we've never known any great wit, or any brilliant person at all except Sir Cantopher—and my brother, like the rest of us, has got used to *him.* Give him time, give my mother time, give even our friend here time,» the girl pursued with a courage that was a match for his own—"though I ask you for no more myself: I don't know whether you've made me blind or made me see as never before, but what I really want is that you shall take me so for granted, in spite of all your odd ways, not one of which I'd now nevertheless have you fail of, that if I'm noticed at all when we begin to go out together, as we presently shall, I shall be noticed no more than your shadow and just according as you happen to cast it!"

This assuredly corresponded for Ralph to his own actual spirit of play, and even went beyond it for the great air it gave her, something akin to which he was hoping he had himself put forth. He met it to extravagance, wanting to know if he hadn't taken *her* for granted with the very first stir of his response from the other side of the world, protesting he'd go out with her on the spot and cast his shadow in any light she should choose; which was at once reflected on, however, in the most anxious admonition that Mrs. Midmore had uttered.

"We'll have our friends here first, please, and it will be your mother. Miss, and not you, who will make our cousin and your relation to him known."

She had gathered herself up for this, though it was visible again to Ralph that if she uttered the proviso for Molly's control, not less than in a high degree for his own, she yet appeared to press it, restlessly and appealingly, upon her son and her other guest, who nevertheless, engaged for the time in considerations of their own, gave it no particular heed. Ralph, at sight and in suspicion of a certain effect produced in her which was the very opposite of what he intended—for this evasion of his aspect didn't come, did it? to his overriding her—blinked for an instant at a splendid impulse, and then fairly lost sight of its splendour in the straightest, friendliest, homeliest application of it; moving from his place straight across to her, laying a hand on each of her shoulders and, with the bravest, kindest face in the world, making as if she should look at him in spite of herself. He had entertained, during these extraordinary hours that he had been in the room (few or many, he couldn't have said which,) a hundred wondrous sentiments, but hadn't yet, to the clearest of his consciousness, been sorry for anyone—which was what he desired under that special stress to testify to his being for this great and distressed, though nobly resisting and now of a sudden coldly submissive lady. Was he going to be sorry for people on any such scale as this accepted prompting portended?—so he dimly wondered, as if it were the last thing that had been in the bargain, even while Mrs. Midmore closed her eyes under his touch and left him fairly to appeal to the others, to her son, to her daughter, to Sir Cantopher himself, whose lids indeed were not noticeably much less narrowed than those of their hostess, for attestation that he meant the very most charming things. If he only hadn't once more, all the same, to wince the while with awareness of that overdone grimace of his own!—he had effectively enough shaken it off some time previous, but his relative's pale rigour, while his action lasted, threatened to set it up afresh! Nothing, however, could have exceeded the respectful form of the freedom he now used. He had kissed her on either cheek, under encouragement offered, on first seeing her, and he at present repeated the homage in conditions that might well have suggested to him that ever so much time, days or weeks instead of mere mixed moments, had elapsed between the two transactions.

"I desire so to conform to your every wish and to renew every assurance. I get every now and then the impression that I'm not quite so much with you, or you not quite so much with me, as you would like me to be, and as I certainly should like to—and then I wonder what's really the matter. Nothing surely is the matter, with our perfect understanding—unless it be that I worry you somehow just from ignorance. Yes, I'm clever"—Ralph kept it up—"but I'm not so sure I'm wise; at the same time that I *am* sure I shall be able to learn not to trouble you if you'll only name to me always at the moment just how I'm doing it."

Marked withal was her oddity of not really meeting his face; he was close to her, he had folded his hands as in supplication the most suggestive, but she looked straight down at his feet. "I wouldn't for the world, sir, take you up on anything. I like too much to listen to you, and you've only too many grand fancies. The great thing is that you like us—for if you like us you won't hurt us." She had a pause, but while he still waited she did at last look up at him. "There," she exhaled; "there!"—and she showed him, clearly wishing to do it, that she could smile a bit convulsively, and with the most excruciating dimness, as well as he; holding up her head, drawing in her lips, meeting his eyes and after an instant letting him see, as he thought, something in them like the strange long look, the questioning fear, that he had just been dealing with in her son. He hadn't hitherto caught in her face any such hint of resemblance, but here she was fairly overcoming something, even something akin to what he knew, or what he at least hoped, that he had just made Perry overcome. There was the pity, his having to think of being sorry; she talked of his "hurting", or rather of his not hurting them, and he'd be hanged if he'd hurt them in whatever disconcertment—he'd himself suffer in any way first; which he was on the point of making, gaily and familiarly, his answer, when it struck him that this would be openly to take account of danger, the idea he sought most to repudiate. So he uttered his cheer, which indeed truly, from the tone of it, might have been his compassion, in another form.

"Keep tight hold of me, don't let go of me for the tenth of a second—as you seem to do when you won't look at me. I'd rather you all stared me out of countenance at once than kept from me, either one of you, the light of your own. It mayn't strike you that I want more encouragement than I've already had, but I feel I can do with every scrap you'll give me, and that if you'll remember as much as that we shall still have a merry life."

"'Still, still'?" Molly caught this up; she had risen again to her highest pitch. "What on earth, pray, has happened that we shouldn't?—and what *can*, you wretch, unless it be that we all die for love of you at once? That's the only thing that may be the matter with us—isn't it, mamma?" the girl appealed; "that you're killing us, I mean, with the wonder of you, and that our mother is apparently the first to succumb. Don't change, nevertheless; don't waver by a hair's breadth from what you are at this moment. I want to show you off—I do, I do; and yet I seem at the same time to want you not to be touched—and don't know how that's to be managed!"

This figure, on her lips, determined in Sir Cantopher the play of comment that Ralph had felt to be gathering force; a remark which sufficiently told him, as it dropped, on which side of the line of confidence in him it had fallen. "You're very fine porcelain indeed, no doubt; but, for myself, I shall like, as you'll see, the sense of handling you with care."

It was after Sir Cantopher had spoken that our young man felt himself measure best the attention he had honoured him with, and how much achieved possession of him was noted in the tone of these words. They were even startling as a sequel to his wait for decision, as who should have said, and it was almost as if they quite supremely clinched for our friend in these few instants the irreconcilability of his various desires to oblige. More and more was it that he had come, that he only wanted and needed, to oblige all round; and while he now expressed, so far as any attitude might, whatever intelligence should be most in order, he had the quick idea of suggesting to the four together that they should try to understand and arrange with each other only, making somehow a common ground and not troubling him about the manner of it. He looked thus in the face the fear of being quarrelled about, and was on the point of breaking out with an "Oh there's plenty of me for you *all* if you›d only believe it and let me see each of you enjoy it!» when Sir Cantopher practically blighted the impulse as by a positive queer revel in that idea of precautions.

"Molly may do what she likes and risk what she likes; she thinks you a wonder and wants to call others to admire, and I think you one too and prefer to be selfish about you—that is to handle you as wisely as wonders should only be handled: we should always know perfectly what we're doing with them. No, no, don't deny it," this eminent judge pursued—"I don't think I should care for you if I really understood you, though I'm at the same time quite willing to believe that when I do understand you, as I hope to on better opportunity, I shall not care for you less. I don't get tired of my treasures, you see—and that's the way to estimate real treasures. We get tired of the false, but see more and more, to the end of time, in the true. I shall nevertheless not interfere," he wound up, turning to Molly—"I shall be so far from wanting him to live only for me, and a monstrous pretension it would be certainly, that seeing how he supports your wear and tear will be half the interest of him, and you must therefore be prepared, my dear child, for my taking still more in yourself than I've perhaps ever yet made you feel."

Ralph broke at once into this with the most nervous of his laughs. "Lord have mercy on us then, how very attentive to each other we're all now going to be! But all I want is that you shan't differ about me—I want you so to agree for your own comfort. I don't want you to like me separately—and in fact don't think I should want you to dislike me in that way either, if you should have to come to it. I want you to like me together"—he talked himself more and more into ease; "I should feel either of you lonely, feel you in difficulties and be sad about you, if one of you, or even two of you, should be moved to any view of me that the others couldn't share. Now don't you call that kind?" he asked of Molly under this growth of assurance; "don't you call that providing for your liking me, and, upon my word, for your hating me still again, with the least trouble to yourselves, since I'm ready to shoulder almost anything?"

The question had the tenderest directness, but once more, for a minute, their common understanding of it, and Molly's own not least, seemed to lapse—his sense was touched by that strange convergent wait. He truly could thus, he should have felt, know at least by renewed experience what it was to feel them united in blankness, make free as he might with those other vanities. It was in the nature of these surprises of their collected wit to be blest in proportion as they were brief, however—and this even though they suggested to him while lasting the question of what would become of him, what would become of all of them, if they did last more than they should. The break was somehow better as coming, if possible, from one of themselves—and now he knew, probably indeed very soon, that it had come in the form of an inquiry of Mrs. Midmore's, made in all gentleness and elegance. "Why is it, please, that you provide so for our hating you? It sounds so dreadfully as if you knew something——!" She pulled up, her words expired, and it was for an instant as if the high and handsome lady, the pitch and sound of whose presence he had so begun with enjoying, had shrunken to a pale, pleading, pathetic person, a person engaged for a moment in the fantastic act of trying to buy him off by conciliation. He had a glimpse of something stranger than any conceivable expression of it—of the possibility, that is, of a fear in her of being frightened, with its instinct of gaining time before the danger increased. She smiled a bit convulsively again—she had done so some moments before; but good it was at once withal that the very delicacy of her dread or her desire could make him glow as with foreseeing pity, another throb of the same queer kindness that had stirred him a while back. Yes, yes, he himself shouldn't have cared to apprehend what she apprehended, however the particular point of it might show; and why accordingly *shouldn't* one be in horror and in pity of contributing to an alarm so gratuitous or in fact, as they said, so false? It was true at the same time indeed that there was no answer to her last imputation which wouldn't leave him still rather more staring at it for himself than brushing it away for her: which was the sense in fact in which he promptly enough replied.

"I ask myself, when you tell me that I strike you as 'knowing' something, what it is I can know that wouldn't be a good deal more to your advantage than to mine if you were to find it out! I don't know anything that I *conceal*," he smiled and smiled; "no, no, no, I seem to myself to know so much more than anything else what I've learnt from yourselves in the last hour or two, that if you were to turn me inside out I can't imagine your coming on the least little scrap that would shock you!" So he spoke, though, carry it off as he would, this plea of his own didn't meet the fact that parts of his consciousness into which he didn't *want* to peep, into which he could positively choose not to, appeared to beset him even while he thus reasoned. And somehow it contributed to this appearance that Molly had, at contact with her mother›s peculiar earnestness, quickly rallied again to the defence of her apparently fond fancy.

"Ah I won't have *that*, sir, again—that you're not in possession of matters of your own which it may be our affair, say, to find out if we can, and yours to keep us from learning if we haven't the courage or the cleverness. I won't have it, as I told you long ago"—and she herself spoke, it oddly struck him, as if it had been a month—"that the character I marry should be a bigger simpleton than I, since of course a young lady bred as my mother has bred me really knows less about the world in many ways than even the most commonplace man, let alone such gentlemen as Mr. Pendrel and Sir Cantopher."

Sir Cantopher took this from her as if she really rendered him a service by associating her two gentlemen in that connection: it so supremely stuck out of him at last that he must desire but to refine, under a strong motive, upon the pleasant propriety of their being thrown together. "Every word you say"—he addressed himself to Ralph—"adds to the pleasure your company seems to promise, and I had best warn you at once perhaps that if you have some singular reason for wanting to appear commonplace you would do well to forswear it at once: your effort to act upon it makes you, you see, so remarkable!"

Still wound up to his amenity then, Ralph yielded to this plea—even if it seemed to breathe upon him afresh that chill of the inevitable, residing now in his so witnessed power to raise to the highest point the forces of attention he excited, the repetition of which, from one quarter and another, hadn't even yet taught him how to carry off the fact that he braved it. For he did brave it, he was braving it, braving it at that very moment in his grimaced understanding with Sir Cantopher, the understanding that his face invited the others also to see he didn't fear. What had been deep within him for weeks and weeks but exactly that measure of it now more and more heaped up and the interest of dealing with which had originally so inspired him? "I'm in your hands, as I've told you before"—he smiled and smiled; "I'm in your hands, I'm in your hands!"

"Ah but don't say it as if I were going to drag you to the assizes or the pillory!" Sir Cantopher gave way to that special shade of his amusement which was somehow all edges and points.

Ralph winced for a moment as one who feels in an offered love-pat the touch of a prickly glove—winced fairly to the extent of again dropping his presence of mind and once more snatching it up. "*Is* that the way I say it?" he asked of Molly with such a flush of tender protest as to make her fix him an instant with the very widest eyes she had yet opened and then come at him straight. She didn't speak as she crossed to him, and it was wondrous to him to feel and to know a few seconds later that this was because the attempt for her would have been but formless sound. She answered him otherwise; her arms were round his neck and her face pressed there, while, with his own gratefully bent to it, he felt her hold him in a clasp of possession that was like a resistance to something unseen. He couldn't for that minute himself speak, though the sense of his clutch articulated would have been "Hold me, yes; hold me close, close, and let us stay this way!" They did stay in fact—or when he next measured time it was as if they had been wholly and incalculably absent: so absent, and for so long, that on his reckoning again with the conditions about him they struck him at once as different and as somehow mastered. Had he literally and in so extraordinary a manner slept in his mistress's arms? There was no one to ask it of but poor Perry—for Sir Cantopher apparently had in the interval departed, Mrs. Midmore attending him out of sight, and Molly, herself aware of that, was already at the door, her hand on it for the moment, holding it open, while her look at him recognised even to extravagance what they had "done"—as if she wanted him to know that she knew it, though with something in it for her too that drove her, as he might feel, before it.

This was not prolonged, and yet Ralph could note, for his bewilderment, that some time must already have elapsed, since there came in to him by the open door, from hall or staircase, no after-sound of Mrs. Midmore's retirement with her friend. That explained itself, however, with his quick apprehension that they would have passed out by the other door of the room, which was ajar, as it hadn't been before, and which communicated, as he was afterwards to know, with other parts of the ample house, including the secondary staircase and his kinswoman's boudoir—he was for the first time in his life really to conceive that last convenience. He was at any rate apparently to be left alone with Perry, not taking leave of the others, but suddenly quitted by them or with Molly, for the next thing, at the most, committing him a little portentously to her brother. For she had in a few seconds more turned her eyes to Perry, who spoke at once as if she had put him a mute question and as if he had caught some sound from below. This sound in fact, as more of it came by Molly's door, reached Ralph sufficiently to explain her brother's lively comment, the liveliest he had yet uttered on anything at all: "It's Nan, it's Nan!"

The words had on Molly a remarkable effect, making her listen hard for a moment where she stood, and then, without as yet meeting again her lover's attention, appear to understand what was happening. As soon as she had understood she sharply closed the door, while Perry repeated his elation, or whatever it was, of assurance.

"She has got here by herself—she has travelled by the coach! She has come up to see him, damn him!" he said to his sister quite as if Ralph hadn't been present.

"'Damn him'?" she echoed, now looking queerly at Ralph.

"Damn *her* then!» Perry cried, but again with a happier frankness than he had hitherto used and as if now at last taking Ralph in on his own account.

"I beg your pardon, cousin—but when you wonder so you must damn somebody!"

"Oh *I'm* quite willing to be damned—if it›s at all better for sweet Nan!" And Ralph addressed this by his laugh to Molly as well, who at present, clearly astounded by her sister's act, if they rightly viewed it, hesitated as to the tone about it which should best conform to that understanding with her lover which she had just renewed. He felt in her as she hovered there a certain nobleness of doubt, and how supremely she was enhanced by all these latter signs of a new strain and stress. It was as if she measured as he lacked matter for doing the extravagance of the girl's step, of which she wished, however, to make neither too much nor too little. She ended after a minute by making nearly nothing, for if she simply said to him, as the rather unexpected issue of her thought, "Give her the right advice—she'd take it from *you!*" this presented the transaction as a brief and inconsiderable thing; almost indeed in the light of Nan's very own motive and with a proportionate readiness involved.

Ralph wreathed himself again in grace. "Why should she take it from me, whom she has never seen and knows nothing about, when she hasn't taken it from others who have so much more title?" So he spoke, but conscious as soon as he had done so that it wasn't really for him to have drawn out the question—it was much rather for him to have kept it as small as she preferred it. He had begun so, hours back, with the reign of felicity, and how the devil came it therefore that he now repeatedly missed that trick? The inquiry did in fact, to all appearance, somewhat disconcert his friend, who still waited long enough there before him to find her answer, which she brought out, as it struck him, with a quick perversity.

"Well then, frighten her straight away again, if you like that better!" With which she simply left him, passing out at once by the door opposite the one she had quitted and closing it sharply behind her.

Ralph turned to Perry in his flush of wonder. "Frighten her away? *Do* I frighten——?»

Perry kept his great distance, but spoke after an instant in the sense of accommodation. "You don't frighten *me*—now. You can't, I wouldn't have it even if you wanted to—which I now guess you don't."

"But why in the name of my dearest interest *should* I?» It was strange again to Ralph, his facing his young kinsman›s so exposed, yet so inscrutable sensibility; yet this aspect of him somehow suggested withal that he mightn't at all prove the person from whom there was most to fear. Why, however, at the same time, did this question of fear, suddenly let loose by Molly in her retreat—for wasn't it a retreat?—seem to flutter about the room, itself a scared bird, and make as if for perching on Ralph's own shoulder? It might verily have been perching as our young man, staring about, plucked a fresh apprehension from Perry. "You don't mean that Molly and I frightened off your mother and Sir Cantopher?"

Perry, though always at his distance, was placed by this almost at his ease. "Molly must answer you for herself—but she doesn't really know much more what to make of you than I do."

Ralph's wide eyes stared his reply still more than his lips could form it. "You don't know what to make of me——?"

"Only she likes nevertheless what you do to her that way as her lover. She's not too afraid of you yet for *that!*" Perry explained with a new authority.

This was extraordinary to Ralph—his having gathered such things to tell from that lapse of their consciousness, Molly's and his own, of anything but their possession of each other. "Oh well, I'm glad I have still that advantage!"—and Ralph kept his laugh at least brave. "But was it because *they* didn›t know what to make of us——?» Perry had really arrived at an approach to clear suggestion. «We›re lovers so accepted and blessed——!» He would puzzle it out, but appealed to his Companion for help.

"No, it isn't that they were shocked at your freedom"—Perry said—"though you *were* free!»

"Then why did they make off?" our young man pressed.

"Well, you must get it from themselves."

"Then is there nothing I shall get from you—as my brother-that's-to-be?"

Perry considered of it, resisting confusion. "I'm not your brother yet."

"No"—Ralph also considered: "not in a single morning!" This exchange, none the less, seemed really to further him, and under the aid of it Ralph kept his stand. "But you like me so."

"*I* like you——?» Perry rather growled it, but it was as if he wondered.

"I mean you all do, and you will, you'll see,—especially if you find you can assist me. It's there," Ralph explained, "that your goodnature will be touched."

"Oh but I thought it was yours we were so much to look to. Wasn't it you," Perry asked, "that was to come so prodigiously to *our* assistance?»

"So I take it," Ralph irresistibly smiled; "and what else in the world is it then that I'm so ready for?"

Perry could still mind his steps. "I don't know that you've been striking me as quite so ready!"

"Not so ready as you expected?" It made Ralph's vision jump. "Do you mean that you want money?"

"Indeed I do, by God!"

Ralph stared in fair elation—such an oddity of relief. "Will you have some now?"

"'Now'——?" Something, at this, looked out of Perry's face as not before—a happier, easier Perry, though still embarrassed and divided and with an awkwardness of wonder that made his kinsman laugh out.

"I mean at this very moment"—and Ralph, with the happy thought, clapped his hand to the right pocket of his trousers. It was under the same sort of prompting with which in the earlier part of his talk there with Molly he had appealed to another pocket for that verified possession of his mistress's portrait which so beautifully hadn't failed him; and he consequently beamed all his renewal of support at Perry on feeling his fingers quite plunge into gold. Also he shone, after this fashion, he seemed to know, without undue surprise. The guineas, or whatever they were, literally chinked to his ear, and he saw, the next thing, that they chinked to his companion's as well—which circumstance somehow made them on the instant a perfect mine of wealth. "How much, how much will you have?" he was accordingly justified in gaily asking—and that even while it also played into his exquisite agitation that the Midmores in general had probably ever held the rattle of one's resources in any pocket a vulgar mode of allusion to them. He was so brightly in earnest with his offer, and so interesting it grew and grew each instant to himself, that he would have been willing they should take it for an American freedom caught in the fact. So if it was one it should be a great one, and Ralph kept this up. "You've only to say, you know!" Perry, his head half bent with his trouble, gazed with a bovine air as from over a fence and under his brows—while Ralph felt such surprise, after an instant, at the degree of his difficulty, which suggested positive physical pain, that superlative soothing seemed none too much. His personal confidence moreover had at the first fine touch of his fortune shot straight up, and he rose with it to an extraordinary height.

"I want you to understand, you see, that there's really no sum you mayn't name——!" And he chinked and chinked.

Perry's breath, as it had more than once done before, came shorter and shorter, but he still stood off. "You carry all your fortune about you?"

"Not all—only a goodish handful, but a clutch can follow a clutch." And he so liked his clutch that he drew it forth and held it high, shaking it in the air and laughing. "Guess what this alone comes to."

Perry glared up at the hidden treasure—the effort of Ralph's hand completely contained it, but as our young man was about to say, "Mayn't I count it down to you?" the wondering eyes shifted, resting at once, Ralph saw, on another object. He heard nothing, and his back was to the door from the hall, which Perry would have seen noiselessly opened and with the effect of an appeal for admission. Ralph watched his face, but waited before turning, waited as if something hung on it, and only advised somehow by what he noted to lower his fist and restore it slowly to his pocket. And then Perry had spoken. "If you've come up for your share, my dear, he vows he's all ready to put it on the table, and you can be served first if you like."

The whole passage, however, was otherwise so soundless that Ralph listened a full minute for the answer to this remark before facing about.

IV

The girl was for the time stillness incarnate; she carried the burden of what she had done very much after the fashion of a glass filled to the brim, held out at arm's length and sure to overflow at the first jostle. What she had been mutely doing as she stood there must have been to beg her brother to refrain from any word that would make her position more awkward, and that she felt some confidence for this might have appeared, the next instant, in her large grave look at his companion, which struck Ralph as a sign of greeting the most intended, and yet at the same time the shyest, ever made him. She might scarce have expected recognition, but she seemed to take him in with so little felt restriction on staring that he measured at once the relief she enjoyed at finding him only with Perry. She had been wound up, he felt, for something more difficult, and now this was blest, was a reprieve, for he was quickly certain that with Perry she could easily deal—all the more that what he had just said to her wasn't the deprecated jog, inasmuch as it didn't at all reflect upon her, but reflected only on their cousin. Ralph had in her presence still a couple more of extraordinarily swift reflections—one of these perhaps the very most immediate, in its sweetness and clearness, that had visited his consciousness of these rich hours and bearing upon the fact exactly that he was her cousin, hers much more for instance than Molly's, in respect to whom the nature of the relative was swallowed up in the nature of the lover; bearing on it so happily that in the course of another moment he had brought out the beautiful sense in his own greeting, which had the effect of reading into hers everything either he or she could have desired. He didn't grin for this, as he had been doing for Perry—he breathed it softly, but ever so gravely: "Cousin, cousin, cousin!" though after it too, with the same gravity, which yet, as he felt even in uttering the words, was a perfect extravagance: "Isn't it great, *great?*"

"Great that we're cousins—'great'?" It had broken her stillness happily and, as he figured, without the jostle of her arm; for again it not only left her intrusion ideally unchallenged, but instantly gave it such importance of ground as could in no way whatever be taken from it.

"Well, what *I* call great,» he returned in the liveliest promptitude of explanation; well aware, on the second thought, that it was one of the wrong kinds of turns, one of those that had made the rest of the family exchange wonderments, but eager, within the moment, to be able to judge whether it hadn't perhaps even positively pleased her.

"He calls things in such ways as you've never heard," Perry declared to her as for further and possibly still more convenient information; which Ralph, rejoicing at the comparative sociability of it, straightway took up.

"Of course I do, I know it at once as soon as I've done it, know it by the sound after, *after*, don't you see?"—he addressed the earnest emphasis only to the girl. "Of course we have different expressions—but I'm going to make *you* like them. I›m going to make you understand them,» he explained in the most serious way.

The happiest thing was that though her appearance had determined in him this sudden earnestness, the confidence shown in her and so quickly heaped up made her break into a smile. "I'm not supposed to understand unless I very much want to. Therefore——!" She only smiled, but it gave Ralph an immediate chance.

"Therefore it's clear that you want to so far as I'm concerned; which it's a grand comfort to feel—for I'm not in the least afraid."

"What have you to be afraid of?" she asked with a readiness that made her brother break in before Ralph could reply.

"You understand between you then, damme, things that I don't!" Which comment, looking from one to the other, he at once and most surprisingly backed up. "You've smashed the great jar at Drydown, and he already knows it, and that you've come up to make your confession."

"Oh I don't in the least know *that!*" Ralph declared. "What I should like to believe," he said to the girl, "is that you've wanted so to see your new kinsman that you've risked the adventure." His rejoicing gravity was at such a pitch in it that she turned, under this address, from pale to red, and that something in the expression thus produced in her, which was like a rush of some purer intelligence than he had yet touched among them all, determined in him the strangest inward cry. "Why she's modern, *modern!*" he felt he was thinking—and it seemed to launch him with one push on an extraordinary sea. He in fact wouldn't have been sure the next moment whether he hadn't uttered the queer words, queer, in their sense, even to his own apprehension; though he was afterwards to take it that they had appeared to find no echo, even if he had himself kept on knowing for the moment more or less what he meant by them.

What he meant and what if the air *had* vibrated to them they would vividly have signified was the very aspect and figure of this slight, fine, concentrated little person, who suffered this last measure mainly indeed as an offered contrast to her splendid sister, and whose appearance was of a fashion so different from any that either Molly or their mother might have set her that she affected him as linked to them but in the degree of one of those sacrificed creatures he had read of in records of the old Catholic world, the oblation made of the plainer and weaker and more thankless daughter to the cloistered life, the glory of God, and the muster in the house of means for no more than one nuptial outfit. All of which, glimmering before him in what was perhaps, if we may choose, his quite most quickened perception, would have married ill with the special intensity of his recognition and qualification had the girl not, by some light and exquisite influence, pleaded against the idea that she concurred in the law of her effacement. She was as sober-hued as any nun, and might well, so far as the material side of her presence went, have been trained to fasts and vigils; but wasn't she rather distinguishably aware of more things in all the world than they, and of different ones from theirs, upon his honour?—so that her longish, narrowish, almost colourless face (with the forehead, markedly high and clear, such as to recall a like feature of some mothering Virgin by Van Eyck or Memling who dimly haunted him, though he couldn't possibly have met her in New York) showed a sort of concentration of consciousness, a strain and degree of expression, which were all that could be referred to as in any way tricking it out.

He had been spending a long time, as it seemed to him, with persons—positively to the number of three—who were indicated to him now as having known, or at least as having been instructed by society, that they were pretty well clever enough for anything they might supposably be concerned with; whereas the light that hung during these moments about sweet Nan, since sweet Nan she at last, and not quite other than disconcertingly, was, appeared rather that of an intelligence rather at sea, or guessing free application to have been so perversely denied it that exactly this mild comfort was what it might have hovered and wavered there to appeal for. They hadn't denied her understanding and Sir Cantopher had in the most pointed manner expressed her possession of it, but if there might have been a sense in Ralph's private greeting to her imaginable energies, it could scarce have helped involving the certitude that the family friend at any rate had read her most wrongly when he had quite most wished to distinguish her. She had suffered from what was wrong, though indeed without being at all pointedly aware of what was right—and this even if it broke upon him as formidable that he should perhaps figure to her as a source of initiation. There were things in her world of imagination, it had taken him so few instants to surmise, which might verily have matched with some of those, the shyer, the stranger, the as yet least embodied, that confusedly peopled his own—though, again, how any such verification of identities, felicities, sublimities, or whatever they might be, could make her "modern" without by the same stroke making *him* so, he naturally as yet failed of attention to discern. He hadn›t, that he knew of, missed from the others any note of their direct command either of their future or of his own; he had only measured some disparities between his and their connection with the past, the effect of his sense of which was that they had the advantage of their perch upon accumulations and continuities more substantially and above all more locally determined. This placed them so little less in the forefront of time that he should by rights at least have appeared to himself comparatively backward in the race—whereby what would there have been in him to make in any special degree for fellowship with this young woman's originality? Never, let us hasten to add, could originality, or any other inspired, independent strain, have more renounced the benefit of a superficial show. The others, as he had seen, weren't proof against bewilderment—which, if she was so different she ought to have been; but the first thing he now next asked himself was how he could ever—let what would come of this precipitated meeting be what it would—press upon her to the least confusion of her at best so troubled fineness. "Modern" was she?—all the more reason then why he should be at once as explanatory as he could. Certain passages of his recent past were affecting him by this time as almost superlatively ancient, and wasn't there one of them that it would at once concern him, in common kindness, let alone common honesty, to make known to her?

"I wasn't aware of your existence," he at all events said to her on taking to himself this perception; "I mean I had never heard of you when I sailed—any more, naturally enough, than when I arrived. It has only been to-day. It came out unexpectedly. But now I'm sure," he went on to the relief of his conscience, of his reason, of his imagination, of he could scarce have said what; to the rectification in any case of something he now knew, the confession made, to have been hurting him like some limb kept in a posture adverse to its function. The gained ease was even too great for joking—he couldn't too plainly state it. "You see I knew all about *them*—or I felt as if I had done so as soon as I got here; which comes to the same thing, doesn't it?" There he was asking her *that*, by the way; as if she could tell him whether or no it came to the same thing. Would he have put such a question to her mother, to her sister, to her brother, or even to wondrous Sir Cantopher? It was the kind of question that tended to produce in them that arrest of intercourse; and, extraordinarily enough, it seemed now to hang but by a hair that it might under this new relation make everything easier. Was she going, sweet Nan, to be drawn to him just exactly by certain features of the play of freedom that he had felt warn the others off? Strange certainly that such a satisfaction should within so few moments have begun to breathe upon him—since as a satisfaction, and quite of the freshest, he should know it, that was beyond mistake; and there was nothing to light the anomaly to any degree in his impression that he should be able to make her conceive him better simply by treating her, that is by simply looking at her even, as if she naturally would. This act would be on his part a more conceiving, if withal a more wondering, thing than any yet—though what had, for that matter, ever been so strange as that the shyest, vaguest, least directly protesting pair of eyes ever raised to him should at the same time submit to search after a fashion that was in itself a sort of engagement? "Don't you think you can persuade your brother to accept an accommodation?" he finally asked.

She hadn't replied to his inquiry about its coming or not to the same thing as a proved case that he should have entertained the fancy of assurances—she had but left the appeal in the air. This, however, hadn't in the least stamped her to his vision as stupid; he had only felt at once how many still other things he could put to her. Here was one as to which he should really like her weight thrown if she would let it be and since Perry had named his occasion; as to which too the idea of the explanatory grew in attraction instant. Clearly she didn't yet understand, none the less, too many things at once awaiting her, and the accommodation to Perry, let alone to herself, not having had time to profit by what had at first been said. Here was something of a tangle, but she cut the knot, after another moment, by the light force of her own readiest pressure. "Do you like my mother and my sister now that you've seen them?"

Ralph stared, for beautifully important as this point had been she suddenly made it more so. "Why, cousin, I'm here as Molly's true lover—to marry her, you know, as soon as ever the banns can be published and her wedding-gown bought: so that what sort of a figure should I cut if she wasn't as dear to me as life? She is greater even than I dreamed."

"'Greater'——?" She hung again on this term as she had done before; but it was as if something had happened since then, and she now met his idea in time. "Won't it be that you'll make her great?"

"I hope with all my heart I shall make her happy, but she's splendid," Ralph gravely, almost sententiously, said, "beyond any power of mine to show her off." He clung to his gravity, which somehow steadied him—so odd it was that the sense of her understanding wouldn't be abated, which even a particular lapse, he could see . . .

Notes for THE SENSE OF THE PAST

[1] The Ambassador *does* of course think him a curious and interesting case of dementia, feels a kind of superior responsibility about him accordingly, is really in a manner «fascinated» and mystified too; and in short quite naturally and inevitably stretches a point to see him, as it were, safely home. This he has it on his mind and his nerves, on his sense of responsibility, effectively to do. But, as naturally, he mustn't acknowledge his conviction, even though Ralph invites him to; and I get I think what I want by making him come down to the street in the cab as from curiosity to test his visitor's extraordinary statement, and then plausibly propose or insist on getting in with him and tracking him, as it were, to his lair: so as to be able to have first-hand evidence of his material situation in the event of whatever further occupation. It's in the street and at the cab door that he makes the point of "seeing home", as if then and there merely extemporised; and with the advantage that I thus seem to get what I remember originally groping for, *having* groped for, when I broke this off just here so many years ago. I gave up taking time to excogitate my missing link, my jump or transition from this last appearance of my young man›s in the modern world, so to speak, and his coming up again, where we next find him, after the dive, in the "old". I think I now have quite sufficiently got that transition—I have it perfectly before me. It passes between them; Ralph himself, on their way, in the cab, or probably better still, outside, on the pavement in Mansfield Square and before the house, expresses all I want; puts it, that is, to his benevolent friend, that he *knows* now perfectly that on opening the door of the house with his latchkey he lets himself into the Past. He disappears into the Past, and what he has wanted is that his companion shall know he is there; shall be able to give that account of him if he is missed or wanted; shall also perhaps be able to take in all, whatever it is to be, that may yet happen, and believe in his experience if he ever rises to the surface again with it. This of course but clinches the Ambassador's sense of the refined beauty of his mania; though at the same time the very law of my procedure here is to show what is passing in his

excellency's mind only through Ralph's detection and interpretation, Ralph's own expression of it—so leaving my own exhibition of it to stand over for my final chapter, my supreme dénoûment, when Aurora What's-her-name, under a tremendous "psychic" anxiety and distress of her own, which has been growing and growing within her commensurately with Ralph's own culmination of distress and anguish in *his* drama, which we so centrally and interestingly assist at, comes out to London for relief and throws herself upon the Ambassador with the strange story of her condition, matching and balancing so remarkably poor Ralph's own story of the number of months before. An essential point is that the time of duration of Ralph's plunge or dive is exactly the real time that has elapsed for those on the surface—some six months being about what I provisionally see. The horrid little old conceit of the dream that has only taken half an hour, or whatever, any analogy with that, I mean, to be utterly avoided. The duration is in short the real duration, and I know what I mean when I say that everything altogether corresponds. Then it is, in the final situation, that we get, by a backward reference or action, the real logic and process of the Ambassador's view of how it has seemed best to take the thing, and what it has seemed best to "do" in connection with his strange visitor's exhibition. He gives, he states, what has then determined and guided him; and I see that he states it to Aurora all sufficiently and vividly, so that we don't have any clumsiness of his going back to it, I mean to his account of his own procedure, with Ralph himself when we have Ralph at last restored and, as what all that has gone on in the interval makes it, saved: saved from all the horror of the growing fear of *not* being saved, of being lost, of being *in* the past to stay, heart-breakingly to stay and never know his own original precious Present again; that horror which his conception of his adventure had never reckoned with, and his manner of *getting* saved from which, saved by the sacrifice, the self-sacrifice of the creature to whom he confesses, in his anguish of fear, the secret of who and what and how etc. he *is*, constitutes the clou and crisis and climax of my action as I see it. It will take more working out, which will come but too abundantly, I seem to apprehend, as I go; but I have the substance of it, I have that still, as I had it of old, in my vision, even if a trifle rough, of the two sisters, the mother, Mrs. So-and-so of Drydown, the brother of that period, and whoever or whatever else I may subordinately need—even to the point very possibly of a second young man, the third, that is, in all, who is a wooer or suitor of the younger sister and, for my full kind of quasi-Turn-of-Screw effect, is of a type, a type of the period, entirely opposed to that of the brother. I see him, I have him and his affair, too thoroughly to have to waste words on him here. The more I get into my drama itself the more magnificent, upon my word, I seem to see it and feel it; with such a tremendous lot of possibilities in it that I positively quake in dread of the muchness with which they threaten me. The slow growth on the part of the others of their fear of Ralph, even in the midst of their making much of him, as abnormal, as uncanny, as not *like* those they know of their own kind etc., etc.; and his fear just *of* theirs, with his double consciousness, alas, his being almost as right as possible for the «period», and yet so intimately and secretly wrong; with his desire to mitigate so far as he can the malaise that he feels himself, do what he will, more and more produce. There must be an importance for him, I mean about him, in the view of the others; and this must be definite and consist of some two or three very strong and vivid facts—vivid that is to the imagination of people of 1820. Rather beautiful does it seem to me to have two or three of his actual modern facts stick to him and operate in this sense that I try to project: notably his "refinement", though he tries to conceal it, to dissimulate it; notably his being in 1820 as "rich" as he is, or was, in 1910—which counts for an immense well-offness at the earlier period. And then his whole true modern attribute and quality, with a distinguished appearance to match it, and certain things dont il ne peut pas se défaire, that are of the modern pitch of material civilisation, like his perfect and soignées teeth, for example, which that undentisted age can't have known the like of, and which constitute a part of his troubled consciousness of complication. He dissimulates, he succeeds, he fits in above all because he pleases, pleases at the same time that he creates malaise, by not being *like* them all; which it is that gives me what I just above threw out this question for, his "importance". Without the importance I don't see the situation for him at all as I want it, and yet I must bring it in on lines of sufficient verisimilitude—even though while I say this the element so visualised fills me with the effect to be got out of it: I mean the charm and interest and fineness of that. In short once I have the importance, as I say, I have everything: the rest all clusters round it. Yes, the more I think of the little man (he must be little) who circles about the younger sister, and of whom she has an intimate horror—*he* rich, by the way, too, and thereby desired by the mother, and with a small sort of raffiné (of that time) Horace Walpole atmosphere about him—but in short I neednֹt talk of him thus; I possess him too entirely. I keep missing, at the same time, all the while, my fact of putting the essence of what I see straight enough thus—the postulate of the young man from America arriving, coming upon the scene, somehow designated or arranged for in advance as to one or other of the sisters (I leave it rough and a little in the air, so to speak, for the moment. The just how and just why I can dispose of in a page when in closer quarters.) The point is that the wrong sister, abetted by the mother, pounces on him, as it were—it's the elder one I see doing this; and it so befalls that he is booked, as we say, to marry her, before, with all the precautions he has to keep, he can, as we also say, turn round. So it is that after a little, after the flush of the amusement of his extraordinary consciousness having begun a bit to abate in the light of the brutalities etc., what I call to myself most conveniently his dawning anguish glimmers and glimmers; what it means to see himself married to the elder sister and locked up with her there in that form of the Past. He conceals, he successfully does so, his growing malaise, all the effort and unrest of which, by the by, makes him, he sees, appear to them "clever" beyond anything they have ever dreamed of (they, also, by the way, must pass for clever, as 1820 understood it;) and I catch also, parenthetically, at my need for their not being, with all their pride of gentility, at all as conveniently well-off as they would like, or must require, this fact helping greatly the importance for them that he is possessed of means that seem to them quite blessedly large. The note of their thrift, a certain hardness of meanness, the nature of their economies, the brutality (I keep coming back to that) of their various expedients—this and that and the other Ralph has to take in. Meanwhile he is committed to the elder sister—and we have the effect on her of his importance, his means, his cleverness, mixed up with that in him which is mystifying to all of them, but which the elder sister at first at least sets down to the action and the play of a cleverness, a strange cleverness from over the sea, such as she has never before conceived. She holds on and on to him even after the malaise, and his sense of it in them, with his still greater sense of it in himself, has quite begun, as it were, to rage; with which: oh I see somehow such beautiful things that I can hardly keep step with myself to expatiate and adumbrate coherently enough. Let me just nail 2 or 3 things, by 2 or 3 of the roughest simplest strokes, in order to catch and hold them fast before I go on. All the while, all the while, the younger sister, who is ever so touching, charming, really appealing for him—all the while, all the while. I know what I mean by this sufficiently just to see and note here that the elder does after a while break off under the action of the malaise, which Ralph is in the extraordinary position of having in a way to work against and being also, as a means of release to him, grateful to. I can't take time to catch at this moment, but keep it till the next chance, my notation of how and where the younger sister, the one who really would have been meant for him, the one for the sake of whom he would almost really swing off backward—my notation, I say (after a break of dictation) of the origin and growth of the special relation between Ralph and herself; she being of course the nearest approach—and in fact it's very much of an approach—that I have in the whole thing to a Heroine. I seem to myself now to have intended somehow, in my original view, an accident, a complication, a catastrophic perversity or fatality, as it were, through which Ralph has addressed himself from the first to the elder, the wrong, sister instead of the younger, the right—and when I try to recover what I so long ago had in my head about this there glimmers out, there floats shyly back to me from afar, the sense of something like this, a bit difficult to put, though entirely expressible with patience, and that as I catch hold of the tip of the tail of it yet again strikes me as adding to my action but another admirable twist. Of course I am afraid of twists, I mean of their multiplying on my hands to the effect of too much lengthening and enlarging and sprawling; but the bit that I speak of now is surely of the very essence of the situation. It connects itself with something so interesting and effective, so strong and fine, to express—from the moment one successfully tackles it. "This" then, what I mentioned above, is that Ralph has "taken over" from the other party to his extraordinary arrangement certain indications that have been needed for starting the thing, and which I think of him as having, under the operation of the whole prodigy, very considerably, very enormously, assimilated. Enormous, however, as the assimilation may be, it is not absolutely perfect, and don't I exactly get out of this wavering margin, this occurrence of spots and moments, so to speak, where it falls short, just one of those effects of underlying distress, of sense of danger, as I comprehensively call it, which are of the very finest essence of one's general intention? He knows his way so much and so far, knows it wonderfully, finds his identity, the one he wears for the occasion, extraordinarily easy considering the miracle of it all; but the very beauty of the subject is in the fact of his at the same time watching himself, watching his success, criticising his failure, being both the other man and not the other man, being just sufficiently the other, his prior, his own, self, not to be able to help living in that a bit too. Isn't it a part of what I call the beauty that this concomitant, this watchful and critical, living in his "own" self inevitably grows and grows from a certain moment on?—and isn't it for instance quite magnificent that one sees this growth of it as inevitably promoted more and more by his sense of what I have noted as the malaise on the part of the others? Don't I see his divination and perception of that so affect and act upon him that little by little he begins to live more, to live most, and most uneasily, in what I refer to as his own, his prior self, and less, uneasily less, in his borrowed, his adventurous, that of his tremendous speculation, so to speak—rather than the other way round as has been the case at first. When his own, his original, conquers so much of the ground of that, then it is that what I have called his anguish gets fuller possession of it—it being so one thing to "live in the Past" *with* the whole spirit, the whole candour of confidence and confidence of candour, that he would then have naturally had—and a totally different thing to find himself living in it without those helps to possibility, those determinations of relation, those preponderant right instincts and, say, saving divinations. Don't I put it at first that he is excited and amused and exhilarated by the presence of these latter, by the freedom with which he lives and enjoys and sees and knows: the exhilaration proceeding during the "at first" time, as I put it, by the sense, the fairly intoxicating and spell-casting consciousness of how the inordinate business is going. His sense of success, which there is just enough of his critical margin or edge to appreciate, to estimate, and thus relate to his former consciousness and his whole starting-point, this *creates* for him a part of the success, the success with the others, by the very spirit and glamour (to them) that it gives him and that keeps up till the change I visualise, the inevitable difference, to phrase it roughly, begins—begins by something that *happens*, something that springs out of the very situation itself for portent, for determination, and which I must work out, or work into, exactly the right dramatic identity for. This I guarantee; but meanwhile I am ahead of my argument, and must hark back for a few minutes to what I left standing and waiting above—that "this" which I was there about to follow up. At once, withal, I see it in images, which I must put as they come, and which make for me thus, don't I seem to feel? one of the first, if not *the* very first passages of my action. An action, an action, an action must it thus insuperably be—as it has moreover so well started with being—from the first pulse to the last. Ralph, taking leave of the Ambassador, the depositary of his extraordinary truth and the (as he hopes) secured connection with the world he cuts himself loose from, dropping as from a balloon thousands of feet up in the air, and not really knowing what smash or what magically *soft* concussion awaits him—Ralph, I say, in entering the house then walks at a step straight into 1820 and, closing the door behind him, shuts out everything to which he has hitherto belonged. He is from that minute, to his own eyes and all his own faculties, the young man in the portrait, the young man we have seen advance to him that night of his vigil in the drawing-room. This bridge or effective transition from the visit at the Embassy to the central drama is thus *found* and is as good as another for my purpose—swift and straight and simple and direct; as I have on a foregoing page, however, sufficiently stated. Well then, I want to make it, *within*, his arrival, practically, from America to the London family: as to which, however, on consideration don't I see myself catch a bright betterment by not at all making him use a latch-key?—to the fact of which an awkwardness and a difficulty would, I seem to make out, or *do*, rather, immediately attach.

No, no—no latch-key—but a rat-tat-tat, on his own part, at the big brass knocker; having effected which he stands there a moment, I think, his head very triumphantly high and confident, looking from the steps down at the Ambassador on the pavement; this latter isolated now, by Ralph's having paid and discharged the cab, which has driven away, the moment they got out. What I glanced at as happening between them just thereafter takes place on the pavement, as I have noted, but with this difference, I see with a minute's further intensity of focussing, that he does—well, what I have just stated. Only I seem to want a dumb passage between the two men while the Ambassador just stands, just lingers, as if now at last verily spellbound. I mustn't forget, by the way, that I have spoken of the rain, or that Ralph has, at the Embassy, and that his Excellency can't be represented as standing there without a vehicle and under his umbrella. So it has been constate on their coming out of the Embassy that the rain has stopped during Ralph's visit, so that it's all the more quite over when they reach the square. The Ambassador has said, in reference to the cab, "Oh I won't keep it—I'll walk home; you've really made me need to shake myself!" Thereby I get him held there for the minute seeing the last of Ralph after the latter has knocked and before the door is opened. Ralph turns on its opening—it is held open wide for the moment, and as I seem to see this altogether in latish daylight of a spring, say of a March or April, season, it is no lighted interior that is for a moment exhibited, but just such a Bloomsbury entrance hall as may very well meet the eye to-day. Within then, Ralph arrives; and what for the moment I want summarily to mark is simply that the elder sister is the first person in the "drama" that he sees. She must be handsome, very—handsomer in an obvious way than the younger; not yet at all in sight—not in sight, I think, till after the three others have been, the mother and the two young men, who a little announce and prepare her. It even may be a little, I think, that she is for the time away from home and doesn't return till after the situation is otherwise started. Well then, here it is that what Ralph *knows*, what he is in possession of and has the general preparation for, is so far precarious and, so to speak, treacherous, that—well, all I want to say now is, before I break off, that he takes her, takes the elder one, for the right young woman. This seems easy—so right, in her way, does she appear to be. He knows, he has "had it", from the 1820 young man, what is expected of him in regard to one of the young women; how, in what manner and on what terms and by what understanding it has come to be expected, remaining questions that I shall adequately, not to say brilliantly, dispose of. What I seem to want is to get the relation between these two started on the spot, before any other relation whatever takes place for my young man; feeling as I do that once it is started I can abundantly take care of it. I even ask myself whether I mayn't have my hero's very first impression, the very first of all, of my second man, as I call him, the one other than the brother, who is there for the second sister and whom he should perhaps do well to find alone in the room when he is introduced, waiting there for the others, the objects of his call, and constituting Ralph's immediate impression. It is to *them*, say, that the first sister enters—so indefeasibly and luminously, as it were, do I see my procedure ruled by the drama, the quasi-scenic movement, or essential march and logic and consistency, at any rate. However, I am not pretending in these words, in this rough scenario, to go into any but the most provisional and general particulars. What I want is that my young man should inevitably and naturally *dazzle*, and become aware of it, by the very force of his feeling the distinction and privilege of the prodigious element that has launched him. The others don't in the least know what it is in him, but what I want to make ressortir from it is that he "does" the other fellow, his ancient prototype, the expected cousin from America, with no end of gentility etc. There must be at the same time, of course I see, enormous foreshortenings, great compression and presentation of picture: I want something of this sort to show before the second daughter turns up. Of course such questions as whether it was of the period that the elder one, bred as girls of that time were bred, would "come down" to a couple of "gentlemen visitors" alone, and as by a kind of anticipation of our current modernity—of course such a detail as that is a perfectly easy thing to handle and make right. At the same time withal, in respect to what I said just above about the scenic, let me keep before me how the very essence of all this is to stick as fast as possible to the precedent of the "Screw", in which foreshortening abounded and I didn't, and couldn't, at all hand my subject over to the scenic. The present is of course a much larger and more complicated affair, lending itself much more to the scenic, even in a manner insisting on it a little, or a good bit; but I must guard, guard and all the while intensely guard, myself, none the less—or I shall sprawl out over ever so much more ground than I shall want, or at all need, for my best effect, to cover. If I may but look it well in the face that the thing can only afford in a very minor degree, not in the least in a preponderant one, to express itself scenically, it takes very little further thinking to see how vital that is, and that the particular effect I want most to catch, that of the crescendo of the malaise, really demands and depends upon the non-scenic for its full triumph. I grasp this entirely; I see how "narrative representation" most permits, most effectively prepares and accompanies, my turning of my present screw, and what a part picture and image and evoked aspect and sense can play for me in that connection.

I catch, it seems to me, with a certain amount of vision already two or three, not to say three or four, of my essential hinges or, as I have called 'em, *clous*, that mark the turns or steps of the action. The first of these is the appearance on the scene of the second daughter after things have got well under way in respect to the first. The first is the fullblown flower—she mustn't be at all too young, by the way; must be going on to thirty, say—and very little trumpet-blow takes place about her, on the part of the others, in advance: all pointing to the fact that she's a sort of neglected quantity—whom nevertheless the little Horace Walpole man does appreciate and pretend to; under all encouragement from the others who think him quite *more* than good enough for her, though not good enough, no, for the elder sister. Beware, by the way, of any little false step here: don›t make the pretender in question too too eligible or, in the modern lingo, smart; since if this were so Ralph wouldn't pass for more desirable. I must keep him a bit down, in the right sort of way and degree, in comparison with Ralph; bearing in mind at the same time that a sort of leading note in it all is his, our's, sense of the hard old class rigour governing the life about him and of which he sees the salience at every turn. The reappearance at home of the second girl, from wherever she has been (expressible in 10 words) at any rate is, as it were, my first clou or hinge; a fact, an impression, an apprehension, that immediately makes such a difference for Ralph. I forget already whether I said just above that the H.W. man talks to him, takes him into his confidence about her, even to the point of recognising to R. that she doesn't care for his suit and has much incurred her mother's, sister's and even brother's reprobation by that attitude. Vividness to R. of the reign of authority at that time, the much harder rule and discipline; and how half terrified at what she is doing by hanging back, by resisting, the poor girl herself is all the while. Her first relation to him is that of her appealing exactly from this rigour; her first impression of him and emotion about him, he sees, he gives us to see, is that of a sudden this fine young American relation is a person who may side with her, may help her, may intervene and back her up in not accepting addresses from a person she can't get over her dislike of. Yes, that's their first basis, and for this appeal Ralph must have been prepared by his own sense of the kind of uncanny, to put it in a simplified way, little personage her aspirant is. They come nearer together on that, they meet on that, they talk, they begin to understand each other on that—very great though Ralph's responsibility in the matter, the matter of backing up her refusal, may be. It's at any rate the way the real relation with them, with him—his sense of the ancient brutality of the others to her, her mother, her brother, her sister, stirring finely within him. She hasn't dreamed herself, he sees, of any real equality of transaction, of relation with him at all; for if the others are under the dazzle, so much the more under it is she. She sees—that is *he* sees *that* she sees; he likes her to like him;—which is what gives her the sense of a privilege she trembles up into the enjoyment of, astonished at herself in her exquisite humility (this so touching to R.) even while doing so, The great thing is that he gets into relation with them, and that by the time he has done so the sense of how he needs it, the dim vagueness as yet of how she may perhaps help him, has begun to work in him. He sees, he feels, I make out, that she, as it were, understands him—though how and why she does demands full specification; that in fine what affects the others as his secret, as his queerness, as what they don't know what to make of in him, does the reverse of putting *her* off—it makes her somehow feel that beneath or within all his dazzle he is an object for pity, for pity «about which» she could perhaps do something. The ideal thing for dramatic interest and sharpness would be that there is just one matter in which, just one point at which, just one link with his other identity by which, he betrays himself, gives himself away, testifies supremely to his alienism, abnormalism, the nature of his identity in fine; the ideal thing would be that, I say, and that it should be definite and visible, absolutely catchable-in-the-act, enough for her to seize it, come into possession of it, and yet not merely terrify or horrify her: affect her in short, on the contrary, with but a finer yearningness of interest. The ideal, as I say, would be that this fact or circumstance should be tremendously right from the tone of the "Screw" point of view, should be intensely in the note of that tone, should be a concrete and definite thing. Find it find it; get it right and it will be the making of the story. It must consist of something he has to do, some condition he has to execute, some moment he has to traverse, or rite or sacrifice he has to perform—say even some liability he has to face and the occurrence of which depends somehow on the state in which he keeps himself. I seem to see it, it glimmers upon me; though I didn't think of it at first—I hadn't originally got as far as it—it hovers before me though in the form of the only thing it *can* be. When I call it a liability I seem to catch it by the tip of the tail; seem to get a sort of sense of what it *may* in a manner be. Let me figure it out a bit, and under gentle, or rather patiently firm, direct pressure it will come out. He is liable then say to glimpses of vision of the other man, the one portrayed in the picture and whom he had had the portentous passage with before going to the Ambassador; he is liable, put it, to recurrences of a sense of that presence—which thus, instead of being off in the boundless vast of the modern, that is of the Future, as he has described its being to the Ambassador, *does* seem to him at times to hover and to menace: only not to the appearance or effect of reassuring or relieving him, but only to that of really quite mocking and not pitying him, of showing him to himself as "sold", horribly sold. Say it's as if the man of 1820, the Pendrel of that age, is having so much better a time in the modern, that is in the Future, than he is having in the present, *his* Present, which is the Past, that a chill and a fear, the growth of a despair and a terror, drop upon him from it and signify somehow that he must begin to feel himself lost. That's it, that's it, that may be admirable, if I can get the right hinge or play for it—which of course I can. He hasn't expected it, I think—unless I represent something of it as coming back to him, while he wonders, from that passage between him and the other fellow which we know, so far as we do know, only by his projection of it to the Ambassador—after our having seen the other fellow approach, that is, at the climax of the first, or the critical, night spent by Ralph in the house. We have come to know something of this later on by our sight of his own mental references to it; so that these relations may quite sufficiently hang together for us. Well, what I want is that once he has the extraordinary experience (the experience *within* the experience) of his being under observation by his alter ego, once he has had it in an acute form and connected it wonderingly with some cause, he feels liable to it again if the same kind of cause shall recur; which by the time the phenomenon takes place has for him much more, as I have said above, a suggestion of menace than a suggestion of relief. That's it—it's as if the other fellow feels, knows, has some incalculable divination, of his, Ralph's *weakening*, while nothing is further from himself *than* to weaken; whereby Ralph connects, as I quite grasp, the consequence with the cause. There must be sequences here of the strongest, I make out—the successive driving in of the successive silver-headed nails at the very points and under the very taps that I reserve for them. That's it, the silver nail, the recurrence of it in the right place, the perfection and salience of each, and the trick is played. I seem to see it thus a silver nail that my young man recognises—well—what he does recognise—when the younger girl (for whom, as for them all, I should do well to provide a name without more delay) swims into his ken, and it's another one, another clou d'argent, when the wave of his confidence seems to have begun to spend itself, doing this, however, in face of something that has taken place. Just what this thing is must constitute another silver nail, and I see it thereby as some symptom given, on the part of the others, of a change of attitude, a change of sensibility, as I must call it, or at least may, for want of a better word. I think it of superior force that they, the others, all except my young heroine, shall begin on *their* side the betrayal of malaise, which Ralph is then affected by; rather than that he should begin it, making it thus that they are by the operation, the outward betrayal, of that condition of his own. Here I have the action of the little H.W., who, moved thereto (I express myself thus roughly) by the situation determined for his own interest through the terms appearing destined to develop between R. and the girl, and this though R. isn't at all free for the girl, opens himself on the subject to the three others and so calls their attention to certain things that they before long find themselves, and confess it to him and to each other, affected too in the sense he communicates. To be perfectly definite it seems to me I must have it that the marriage of Ralph and the elder daughter is definitely arranged and fixed for a tolerably near date; since I want the elder girl, "under the effect," to break off something, and there is nothing so good for her to break off as their engagement. The rupture of that, with R's apprehension of how and why it is coming and has come, is of course a silver nail of perfect salience; just as it is another, I see, that this catastrophe, or whatever one may call it, places Ralph and the younger girl face to face as they have not yet been placed. Their recognition of that, his at least, which is also a perception and a comprehension of hers, what has *this*, in its concreteness, but one more silver nail? What I see myself, at the same time, here concerned with is the question of the outward footing Ralph remains on, finds or makes possible, with the two other women etc. when the rupture developes and after it has occurred. I can't have it end the relation, everything so collapsing—so that there must be still grounds for the relation, and they must be strong and positive, or at least definite and presentable. I get something by the provision that the engagement has not been given out nor the marriage announced as to take place; which, meanwhile, is not at all natural unless some advantage not to be too lightly sacrificed is involved with their still superficially keeping on. This requires thinking of, but doesn't in the least defy handling; and indeed I think I get it at a stroke by the fact that they all cling to him, in a sort, even in spite of the malaise, by reason of the convenience proceeding from his means. Decidedly, yes, they must be, through disorders, extravagances, turpitudes or whatever, of the late head of the family, and vraisemblablement through like actualities on the part of the son who has succeeded him in the proprietorship of Drydown, they must be on a hollow and quaking pecuniary basis—which makes Ralph have to have money, even though this wasn't in the least a *common* felicity or luxury in the American world of that period. None the less were there *some* fortunes, without overstrain of the point, and in short I have only to make Ralph all disposed, very peculiarly disposed indeed and very particularly inspired and inwardly needing and wanting, to pay his way handsomely, to be the free-handed-from-over-the-sea relative of the house, in order to pick up whatever link might have seemed missing here, and make it serve my turn. He pays his way, he regales and "treats", right and left; and nothing can be more in the note of the time I give him the sense of than the extraordinary readiness he finds in everyone to profit by this, the want of delicacy and dignity, by our modern measure, in the general attitude toward pecuniary favours. The smaller still lives on the greater, the minor folk on the great, and Ralph literally sees himself, feels himself, enjoys in a manner feeling himself, figure verily as one of the great by his taste of this play of money-patronage that is open to him. There it is: if I get a clou d'argent by the rupture, in short, I get another, still another, by some "dramatic" demonstration of the fashion after which they are going in spite of their malaise to hold on to him as beneficiaries of a sort. Yes, yes, yes, I have it, I have it: the brother has borrowed money, borrowed it of him bravely, from the first; and the brother opposes the rupture of the marriage for fear that, a complete rupture thus also involved, he will have to pay up to his creditor, his so probably indignant creditor, in consequence of the changed situation. The other two women know this, and what it means for him; and then thereafter see that it needn't mean what they fear, what *he* fears, and isn›t going to—for here I just get a sublime little silver nail in the fact that Ralph, comprehending this, beautifully seeing the way it may help him, quite seems to show on the contrary that he won›t push his hand, won't expose their private gene; seeing what he can get for himself by not doing so. Doesn't he in fact even "lend" the brother more money, lend it after the very rupture, in order to reassure them and keep on with them and show he doesn't "mind" the breach on the part of the elder girl?—this all because it keeps him along and on the footing of his still possible relation with the younger. In plain terms mayn't one put it that he buys, pays for, in hard cash, the pursuance of his opportunity?—as well as put it that his "dramatic" assurance of this, with its readjustment of his footing, constitutes again a silver nail. (There's nothing, I think, that one must so keep before one as that at first he is made ever so much of—much more of than he could at all have hoped.)

Well then, there he is with the question of the marriage ended—as to which, let me catch myself up to remember, I shall have to give *her* a motive, a presentable ground, since it›s ended by her act, which won›t make it too anomalous on his part that relations with the house are kept up. I must have him, by the way, not "stay" with them—I see advantages and naturalnesses, facilitations of several sorts, in his not doing that, but, much rather, putting up at one of the inns of the day, or better still in a lodging in one of the old Westend streets. Why not let the young woman make it quite frank and outspoken—happy thought!—and say in so many words that she can't marry him because, heaven help her, she's afraid of him; just that, simply afraid of him, even if he (with his own malaise at this note) can't get out of her any *why*, when he challenges her, as in dignity and decency he must, for a reason. This much affects and impresses him—for there isn't in it, mind, the smallest hint or implication of its being through any jealousy of her sister, whom she doesn't so much as honour with a suspicion. (The sort of Cinderella quality, so to call it, of the younger one, to be shown as more or less felt by him.) The position thus taken with practical suddenness by his prospective bride is the first definite note, at all really sharp one, that he has to reckon with on the subject of the queerness that hangs, that may so well hang, about him; and it sets up thereby the beginnings of the great feeling that I want to impute to him. He thinks all the same, at first, he expects and apprehends, not with pleasure, however, that this attitude of hers won't be supported by her mother and her brother: the thing having taken place between themselves only, and quite abruptly; she striking him as acting by her own sudden impulse alone, and in a manner not at all to suit the others. They will overbear her, he imagines; her mother in particular will bring her round again and into line. He positively fears this even—so that his surprise is great, and his malaise even greater, when the mother, with a full opportunity, by this time, doesn't so much as speak to him on the subject. There must be a passage between them, him and the Mother, in which he wonderingly and observantly, watching now all symptoms and portents, as it were, waits for Mrs. So-and-So to speak, to broach the matter herself, to show him her knowledge of what her daughter has done. He must know, or must believe, that she has now the knowledge—this point having been treated between him and the daughter, as it were, in the scene of the rupture. He *has* of course to ask her if she throws him over with her mother›s privity and approval, to which she replies that she doesn›t, up to then, that she has broken down but then and there, but that now at once of course she will report herself, so to speak, to her mother. I see it must be the case that she is plain and honest, not at all tortuous or perfidious, and so far as calculating, why calculating quite boldly and confessedly, as to the material advantages accruing; and thereby the more eloquent as to the inward feeling she can't surmount when she renounces these advantages so flatly. Well, the point is, from all this, that our young man is waiting for the mother to express to him that he mustn't on his side take advantage of the girl's backing out, but insistently claim his right not to be so trifled with (the attitude of the family being that they are, for all their straitened means, great people themselves, greater truly than he, and with a greatness for him in the connection,) and is going on as if nothing has happened. He has expected from her, as in character, the information that she has dealt herself, and with the high maternal rigour that then prevailed, *with* the ridiculous child, whom she has thus reduced again to reason and docility. But nothing of that sort comes—the lady of Drydown not only doesn't break ground to him herself in that sense, but betrays to his now considerably excited imagination a fear that he will: which will be, truly, awkward, embarrassing and even "scaring" to her; so that what I seem to see happening is verily that when he thus watches her not speak, notes her as forbearing to for reasons of her own, he doesn't take her up on it, decides in fact not to, decides that the question is really had out between them without either of them so speaking, and only by his looking her very hard in the eye, and her so looking at him, and his keeping it up on this and her keeping it up on that. It simply drops thus, by its own force, the question of the marriage, and the fact that he doesn't have it out, and that she allows him, as by taking care, no opportunity to, constitutes another silver nail, likewise, of as good a salience as I could desire. There it is then, so far as that goes; and after I have dealt for an instant now with the question of what the brother's attitude also is in the connection, I see I shall have got what I was reaching out for considerably above, *the particular thing taking, or having taken, place* which must serve for me as the determinant of the phenomenon, the factor, I have settled to tackle. The «other fellow appears» to Ralph, and makes him ask himself why, contrary to all consistency or logic, the laws of the game, this extraordinary occurrence should take place. He feels it as portentous—feels it, I see, in a way altogether different from the way in which he felt it on the first great occasion; when it only uplifted and thrilled him, making him conscious of all his force—whereas it now disquiets and alarms him, makes him sound it for its logic and its reason; which he clearly enough interprets to himself. A difficult and intricate thread of exhibition here, but as fine and sharp as I require it if I only keep it so. It comes back to him, it comes over him, that he has freedom, and that his acting in independence, or at least acting with inevitability, has laid this trap for him—that he has deviated, and of necessity, from what would have happened in the other fellow's place and time. What would have happened is that *he wouldn't* have feared his prospective bride, he being the other fellow; and that thus he, Ralph, has done the other fellow a violence, has wronged the personality of the other fellow *in him*, in himself, Ralph, by depriving him of the indicated, the consonant union with the fine handsome desirable girl whom the 1820 man would perfectly and successfully have been in love with, and whom he would have kept all unalarmedly and unsuspiciously in love with him. Deviation, violation, practical treachery, in fact—that is what Ralph's production and his effect on the two women (the mother sharing so in the "off"-ness of her daughter) amounts to and represents for him, aggravated moreover by the interest taken in, the community of feeling enjoyed with, the younger girl—for whom, putting it in rough summary fashion, the other fellow wouldn't have cared a jot. I cling thus to, I work thus admirably, what I have called Ralph's insuperable and ineffaceable margin of independence, clinging taint of modernity—it being by his fine modern sense that the exquisite, the delicate, the worthy-herself-to-be-modern younger girl has affected him, in utter defiance of any capacity on the other fellow's part to appreciate or conceive any such value in her. Off in his inscrutable fact of being and of action the other fellow then has had too *his* insuperable margin of antiquity, as opposed to modernity, his independent sensibility, though of a simpler and ruder, a harsher and heavier sort; and it is as a hovering messenger of this that my young man has, so to put it, drawn him down upon him. There it is—I get so my cause of my effect; I get my fact that the other party to the agreed—to experience turns up, all unexpectedly, all "alarmingly" to *my* party after a fashion to show that violence, that injury, as above formulated, has been done him, and as a protest against its being done further. I mustn't have this fact, I see, as repetitive, mustn't cheapen it with recurrence; must only have it, I seem to grasp, take place three times, each time with its own weight of meaning for that time, and then not take place again. It becomes thus each time a clou d'argent of the very sharpest salience. I see the first time as what one may call a warning. I see the second—taking place after Ralph has told the younger girl of what has happened, and what must take place between them on it *has* taken place—I see that as a retribution, or in other words as a thumping, a tremendous aggravator of malaise; and I see the third as something which I will state in a minute after having said a word more about the second. The second constitutes—by which I mean the occasion of it does——a reflection of the intimacy, or at least the beautifully good understanding, with the younger girl, determined for Ralph by his opening himself to her after the sensation, just above formulated, proceeding from the rupture and the way the two other women have acted about it. It's only at this moment, and from this moment, that she becomes his *confidante*, all the difference being made by that; and don't I see it as an enormous little fact that whereas he goes on in silence, as it were, with the others (putting the two men out of the question, which is a point to be treated separately,) he finds her in no ignorance, either real or pretended, but welling up, virtually, with readiness to let him see that she knows. She *knows*—and I think he doesn't even quite understand why or how she knows; her possession of what she does know striking him as a matter beyond, in its "quality", any communication of it that the others may have been capable of making her. The passage between them representing all this becomes then the determinant of what I have called the retributive, as distinguished from the merely warning, reappearance of the other party. I just want to tuck in here provisionally, and before breaking off for the day, that I hold tight the "motive", the dramatic value, of the third reappearance; which resides in my heroine's relation to it—that is not, definitely not, in her having it at all herself, that is not at all directly, but in her becoming aware of *his* having it and, as it were, catching him in the act of the same. Work this out, express this better, or at least entirely, in my next go: I perfectly see it—it only wants clear statement.

I want the business just glanced at, in the four or five foregoing lines, to be as ideally right of course as it can possibly be made; want to squeeze all the effective virtue out of it, in the sense of my generally intended colour and tone, generally intended production of the "new" frisson, as artfully as can be managed. Focussing on it a bit I seem to catch the tip of the tail of the right possibility—though on further thought indeed I am pulled up a little, not being sure it can't be bettered. For I was thinking a moment that she *should*, after all, have herself the direct apprehension, perception or, speaking plainly, vision; have it in the sense that she exhibits herself to R. at a given moment as plunged in stupefaction or confusion by having apparently seen him in double, that is seen him, been sure of him, in a place where, in the conditions gone into or examined and discussed between them, he couldn't possibly have been. In other words she has it to tell him—that to her perception as well, by her experience of it the hour ago or whatever, he rose before her for certain moments in a reality with which everything proves in conflict. That, I say, was what a minute since glimmered upon me—Ralph's having it from *her* as the form of what I call in this connection my third big determinant. But no, but no: what is immeasurably better than that he should have anything of the sort through herself is that she shall have it all absolutely through him. Pressing harder and more intelligently, I come back to the image, the so obviously finest, of her *catching* him under the squeeze, under the dire apprehension, of this third occasion—which I seem to see I can make adequate and operative by her recognising him, just that, after the right fashion, as doing his damnedest *not* to show her, not to betray to her, his intelligence of what he has to infer from, to read into, seeing it in an awful light, something that has just befallen him. It seems to me that I get it and give it, for my best interest, by our having it *all* in the form in which her taxing him with being in a state, a state that she divines, yet but only half understands, determines his at last more or less abjectly confessing to. He breaks down under the beautiful pity of her divination, the wonder of her so feeling for him that she virtually knows, or knows enough; and the question is here of course, isn't it? whether for full lucidity of interest, full logic of movement, he doesn't let her know all or, in vulgar fictional parlance, reveal his secret. That's what it comes to, what it *has* to come to, very much indeed it would seem; that›s what the situation would seem to mean, would appear to have to give, as who should say, of finest: their being face to face over all the prodigious truth—which I think there ought to be a magnificent scène à faire in illustration of. The beauty, the pathos, the terror of it dwells thus in his throwing himself upon her for help—for help to "get out", literally, help which she can somehow give him. The logic, the exquisite, of this to be kept tight hold of, with one's finger on every successive link of the chain. But voyons un peu the logic; which, expressed in the plainest, the most mathematical terms possible, is that what this "retributive" admonition signifies for him is, he feels, that he is going to be *left*, handed over to the conditions of where and what and above all *when* he is; never saved, never rescued, never restored again, by the termination of his adventure and his experience, to his native temporal conditions, which he yearns for with an unutterable yearning. He has come to have his actual ones, the benighted, the dreadful ones, in horror—and he just lets her know *how* horrible everything that surrounds her, everything that she herself is surrounded with and makes part of, have become for him, and under what a weight of despair he sinks if what has just again for the third time happened to him means that his fate is sealed. He breaks down to her, has the one outward, the one communicated despair that I see for him in the course of the affair; his throwing himself upon her for what she can do to avert that doom, his beseeching her, all selfishly, to help him. I say *all selfishly* for the dramatic, clumsily so to call it, value, working value, of this; connected, identical, as it is with his readiness, in fact his intense hope of being able to, profit by the idea of a liberation for him purchased on her part by some sacrifice—sacrifice, by no means sufficiently, of any hope of *him*, but of the very stuff of herself, and this up to the hilt. The more I look into this, the more I see in it; but with proportionately much therefore to be stated about it with a supreme lucidity. Reduced to its simplest expression the case stands that he has fallen in love with her—done so in absolute rebound from the distress that her sister's, her mother's, breach has brought to an end for him; leaving him *originally* to throw himself so much on *her* by reaction, by already acquired and assimilated sense that with her, too blessedly, almost *any* ease for him, whether but comparatively or absolutely, is possible. Thus had he given way to his having, as who should say, fallen in love with her; and thus does that fact work, to his perception, both toward his prime relief and toward his understanding of what he has to fear. Here I come to something pretty intricate and difficult, yet full of life and force, say frankly of beauty, if I can get it straight; which is what I must proceed to. *Why* has what passes, what has passed up to then, between this pair, *why* does it bring on or draw down the third, the «retributive» recurrence? Well, let us see if we don›t make out, and thereby but store up still more beauty and intensity. Put it simply for the moment that the Predecessor has been in love with the elder sister *while*, all unknowably (at the time,) the younger has been in love with him. That condition on her part, it appears to me, gives the link I want, the exact one, for what Ralph finds of prepared, as it were, of reciprocal, of ground laid, for his first understandings with her *when once he has begun to feel* the interfering malaise of the others. I am here, I quite recognise, brought up against the question of why if the Predecessor has been so in love, then and there, in the old time, he should have had this impulse to swing off into conditions so remote from those of the object of this sentiment. I get partly in answer to this the fact that Ralph, shown as so much in love in the first Book, has all the same embraced his opportunity to swing off into where we now have him; but I want something more than this, and I don't get it by simply leaning strongly on the attachment inspired in the man of 1820; inasmuch as the more he has been attached the more explaining will the matter take, the matter flowering into that inordinate phenomenon of the original nocturnal meeting of the two men. If I give full value to the idea that the present Pendrel's pressure, his hovering, penetrating force has had much the most to do with what has taken place, that though the man of 1820 has drawn the man of 1910, exact, (though as to this I must make no modern date explicit of that) back into his own age, while the latter has drawn the former forward into *his*, though I do this, I take care, I soigner the effect that Ralph has begun it, has exerted the original force, has been the determinant for the other and thrust at him his opportunity. This in a general way clears up a little the particular aspect of the case that I am turning over; but don't I still nevertheless want something more than that? I want something that the predecessor may affect Ralph as definitely uttering to him and direfully reproaching him with; and perhaps as I dig into my material and insist on gouging what I want out of it I meet this ground of resentment and reprobation for the predecessor that he feels, or rather that Ralph feels him to feel—for it can all only be *imputation* on R›s part—that he isn›t, as it were, playing the game; ceases quite to play it from the moment that he inspires the elder girl, whom one had hit it off so with dans le temps, with the alarm of distress and dislike that has operated for her rupture. I find something in that, I find I think enough in that—find it enough that Ralph recognises himself as under displeasure, under vindictive displeasure for not, as it were, playing the game. Let me make him put it for himself that the other man doesn't play the game either, from the moment that he thus "comes in", reappears, as it were, as with the conscious purpose so to "brouiller" things. Have it clear that Ralph has no theory at all of what his double's situation is off in *his* sphere; put it that he is by way of having no sort of constructive or inferential or divinatory notion of that at all: which it would make an extraordinary complication to undertake to give him—by which I mean an impossible one, an unspeakable tangle, within the limits, altogether. Yes, yes; the more I think the more I seem to see this conception of Ralph's to be that the other fellow is endangered and incommoded in his sphere by what strikes him as R's practical perfidy and non-accomplishment. What makes this is that the two women, the two other men etc., and the object of his preference above all, are thereby handed over to their intensity of malaise—I give Ralph as seeing and feeling and understanding him as *rendered* thereby vindictive, as convicting him accordingly of «perfidy», and of decreeing the punishment which shall consist of not coming to his help: as I must show it as having figured in their original entente that each shall come au besoin to the help of the other. Out of this little store of indications, at any rate, I shall be able surely to help myself to whatever in the connection, and in closer quarters, I find my best interest in.

Definite it is then that, caught by his young friend in the fact of his *intelligent* alarm he makes a clean breast to her of what he feels and understands, of what his intelligence most helps him to, of what, in a word, it is necessary that she shall know—know in order to assist and relieve him, do the particular thing that *will* so act for him: and so bring the whole situation to the point of its dénoûment. What is then this particular thing?—what can it be when I bring it down to a finer point, that is bring the question down, than my general first notion brought it to? Here the very closest and finest logic must govern all one's sequences. Altogether important and indispensable is it that he doesn't "confess to her", really appeal and throw himself upon her, till she has so "caught", as I say, and cornered him, that there is nothing else for him to do—that is that under the pity and perception and beauty of this he absolutely can't but give in. I have provided above, or sought to, for the motive force establishing in her this capacity—I have sought to do so, I repeat, though I'm not sure I don't still feel a little uncomfortable at being able to do nothing better for her, as would appear, than simply recognise his woe. The beautiful thing would be for her to be able to *refer this woe* to some particular, some portentous observation or constatation already made by him: which question I examined and turned over above without breaking down my objection to her directly sharing his vision: I at that point stated that I wished her but indirectly, but derivatively, to do that—through her apprehension of the state into which it has put him. I seem to feel that this then isn't quite ideally adequate or good without I know not what *more* for her: the ability in her, say, to *challenge him first* on some entirely concrete matter which has told her something for herself, something strange and prodigious, or at least deeply mystifying, in advance of the pressure brought to bear by her on him as an indicated, approved, a revealed sufferer, the pressure in fine that makes him break down. The trouble is that so I swing back again this way to too near the objection-ability, and thereby ask myself if there isn't a way out, a happy thought, in making her, instead of seeing something more than the normal, making her, as I have used the term, "catch", catch in the fact, something in excess of it, see something *less*, have the queerness of *missing* something—her miss of which needs to be explained. The miss, as I call it, corresponds and matches with his exposure to the retributive visitation, as I have called it; and something glimmers out for me in the way of the very occurrence itself, the fact of the visitation for him being marked, marked startlingly and mystifyingly to her, not by his experience as in any degree detected by her, discernible to her, but by his apparent exclusion from *any* experience; or in other words by an inexplicable lapse or suspension of his state of being at all. I think that if I can arrange that—her not finding him present when by all the laws and the logic of life he should *be* present, and so having to challenge him for an explanation—in short I believe I do so see something. He is extinguished for her senses by being in the grip of his face-to-faceness with the other man; and don't I make it out as arrangeable that this takes place in the very fact of his having appointed a tryst or rendezvous with her, at which she has found him, but in the midst of which he then astoundingly fails and, as it were, evaporates? I seem to see something like her having gone out to him by appointment, at dusk of evening, in the Square, the enclosed square itself; where as she approaches she has recognised him within, has even spoken to him through the rails, while he awaits her, and there has had an exchanged word or two with her, directing her round to the gate: which she reaches and enters the enclosure by only to become sure, after moments and moments and moments of surprise and stupefaction, that he is definitely *not there.* I think I have it, it is then; it is at these moments, I mean during them, and under the «influence» exactly, upon the other man, of the appointment given her, that the «retributive visitation» takes place. So I get it, get it enough, get in fact all I need. The visitation over he is in the place again: he is there before her and what more natural "challenge" can I have for her than her alarmed question, that is her stupefied one, as to what in the world had during those moments, which I can make as long or as short, for intensity, as I like, what in the name of unanswerable wonder had become of him. He is there before her again, but before her with what has happened to him overwhelmingly marked upon him.

I see what then takes place between them as a virtual counterpart, in the way of his telling his story, to his scene with the Ambassador, the whole contents of Book III; only all in the note of his depression, his unspeakable homesickness for his own time and place—whereas the other whole passage had been in the note of his elation, eagerness and confidence. He makes, as I say, a clean breast to her—as he had made it under the then essential restriction to the Ambassador; with the immense difference, however, that whereas the effect in the latter case was to impress his then confidant with his being out of his mind, the present effect is, marvellously, prodigiously, to make our heroine believe in the truth of his extraordinary case, recognise how he puts it to her so because he is, because he has remained, exactly so sane, and that it is (prodigiously, marvellously as the force in her to do so may be on her part) to his sanity, exactly, to his convincing consistency, that she rallies. This rallying of hers is of course *the* very point, for interest and beauty, for the climax of the romantic hocuspocus, of my sought total effect; the very flower, so to speak, of what I noted a little back as my scène à faire. As I have already said repeatedly enough, he tells her all, tells her all, all, all; which involves of course his telling her what he feels, has come to feel, in his being so "cut off", so now conclusively and hopelessly cut off, from the life, from the whole magnificent world from which he is truant, unless something, something *she* perhaps can think of, may yet save him. His whole position becomes thus the plea to be saved, to be liberated—with his waiting on her devotion, her affection, her ingenuity, in a word her inspiration, somehow to let him off. All sorts of things to be done with this, in the beautiful and curious and interesting way, especially with the idea that she is sole among those of his actual life whom contact with him, the relation with him, doesn't now make "afraid". Of course this absence of fear on her part has to be based, has to have its own logic in order to have all its beauty; and when one asks oneself *why she*, why she only, thus extraordinarily, one seems both at once to be reduced for support, for illumination of it to the fact that she loves him, and that her affection can do it, and to the concomitant recognition that it will, that it *must*, serve. For it is what exactly and immediately supplies to the situation between them the idea of her being able to operate somehow or other by sacrifice, *her* sacrifice, and of herself and her affection and her interest, somehow or other; so far as one doesn›t make her interest, her interest in *how* to do it, by its very intensity and, so to speak, curiosity, an inspiring motive. I must have had him put it to her straight, How, how, *how* can you get me off, can you release me from this apprehension of having really lost all I feel and fear I›ve lost?—so that thus she has to throw herself back *upon* herself under pressure of this dire appeal which involves, obviously, her using everything. For it would seem to me kind of sublime that he now, at last now, opening up, opening out, everything that he has had before to keep back, tells her such things about those fruitions of the Future which have constituted his state, tells her of how poor a world she is stuck fast in compared with all the wonders and splendours that he is straining back to, and of which he now sees only the ripeness, richness, attraction and civilisation, the virtual perfection without a flaw, that she stands dazzled before it and can only be shut up in the heartbreak of remaining so far back behind it, so dismally and excludedly out of it, while he, with her assistance, shaking her off after he has, as it were, used her, wins his way back to it and out of her sight and sense for ever. Immense and interesting to show him as profiting by her assistance without his being thereby mean or abject or heartless; in which light my affair can't afford, given the whole romantic note of it, to place him. Besides the "psychological" truth and consistency here may back me to any extent. The great question is then *of* her «assistance», how it›s rendered, what it consists of, how he can take it from her and how she can give it. I feel that my subject contains the exact, the exquisite rightness for this deep in its breast, if only I watch hard enough to see said rightness emerge—emerge as it were of itself and as from the operation of what surrounds it. It dwells somehow deep in the fact, the great dramatic fact of the whole business, that she alone hasn't had the mistrust, the malaise and the fear; in connection with which I seem to see something of no small, in fact of the greatest, pop out at me. If he has made her his full "confession" don't I make out that, to balance this, she also tells him about herself something of the last intimacy—not merely how she loves him, but something better still than that?—don't I in fact find myself just leaping and snatching at the idea which answers all my questions of procedure and has my perfect solution just locked up and waiting within it? What is more than her confessing to him that she loves *him*, what gives the exhibitional further twist I was groping for, is that she tells him she has loved the man he is a substitute for, the man of 1820, the *real* one of that actual year, and that in loving himself she has but obeyed the irresistible continuity and consistency involved in his force of representation. I seem to see really my ideal rightness in this—but must keep my head to state here what I see, for my perfect use, roundabout it. I have already spoken, far above, of her having loved the other man, the "real" one, and done so as by the implication that Ralph knows it, is in possession of it, and has seen for himself what an identity and what a connection reside in it. By what means, however, has he originally known it, learnt it, got into possession of it?—unless by one of the others' having stated it to him. I ask myself which then of the others—but only at once to recognise the matter as already determined for me by what I have threshed out. He gets the knowledge effectively and, as I call it, dramatically, to all intents and purposes scenically, by the fact that the little H.W. man, as I call him, betrays the wanted jealousy of him from the moment the elder girl breaks off from him. Up to that moment not, but after it, and on his turning to the younger, with whom the little H.W. man is, as I have shown, himself in love, *then* entirely. This jealousy is practically what leads to his profession of the truth; so that there can be no question of his needing it from her—he so reads it in her manière d'être—up to the time of, and the great revolution constituted by, the scène à faire. What we get thus is her manière d'être for him, all sufficient, all infinitely touching, before that *scène*, and her condition and her action *after* the same; which are two quite different things. *Then*, I mean in this latter case, her avowal, the only entire and direct one, is quite a different thing; out of which I have to pull, as I say, quite what I want. She has loved the man of 1820 *all in himself*—keep every shade of discrimination here flawlessly clear. She has loved him wholly without reward of course, and even under his more than indifference, his degree of contempt; entirely addressed as he was, and has been, to her elder sister. Yet I pull up too here, in the midst of my elation—though after a little I shall straighten everything out—to see that I introduce an element of confusion in trying to work the matter out as if anything can have *preceded* Ralph›s own, Ralph›s «conscious» arrival. Awfully important, and not a little difficult, here, not to let any tangle or any embroilment lay its insidious trap. Doesn›t Ralph know by his own experience, if he takes up the action from the moment, and the moment only, of "arriving", arriving for the first time, all that has happened for his predecessor and exactly what hasn't? There, however, I gasp with relief, is a question that would be embarrassing to me only if, on intenser reflection, I didn't see that I exactly haven't pretended that he doesn't *repeat*, repeat up to a certain point, the experience of the young man of the portrait? Just now, a page or two back, I lost my presence of mind, I let myself be scared, by a momentarily—confused appearance or assumption that he doesn't repeat it. I see, on recovery of my wits, not to say of my wit, that he very exactly does; without which where is definitely that Past, that made and achieved, that once living and enacted Past which is the field of his business? He deflects in the midst of it, yes, by the uncontrollability of his modernism—that is, at least, by what was incalculable beforehand, the exhibition of the way in which "they" were going to take it. The whole effect of my story is exactly his disconcerted and practically defeated face-to-faceness with the way in which they do take it—a matter, a fact, an appearance, that gives me all I want for accounting for his deflection. Thus is our having, his having, everything *en double* regulated and exhibited: he is doing over what the other fellow has done (though it acts for the other persons in it as if it were the first time—this quite all right, though not looking so at first)—and that accordingly hangs together and stands firm. Therefore accordingly my start, a little above, at being what I there for a moment called disconcerted and defeated was groundless: I was going on perfectly straight and right—and am now doing so again. To repeat, accordingly, I get my full right to deal as by a free hand with that little historic truth of the girl's concealed sentiment for the other fellow, accompanied with her equal consciousness that he doesn't and can't and won't care for her a bit: at least in the same way. This revolution that has taken place for her—and well before the scène—of Ralph's differing so from the 1820 man—in short, in short. Note what occurs to me as to the question or no of whether the portrait, the portrait *in* the house in 1910, is done from Ralph in 1820 or not, done from Ralph himself, or accounted for, as coming into existence afterwards. *The* thing, at this ragged edge, is to keep hold of the clue, as tight as possible, that I have grabbed for my solution in the line of her *making* the sacrifice; making it all with a sublime intelligence *for* him, on account of what he has told her of his own epoch—which she stares at in her deprivation.

To clear up a little the page preceding this, instead of doing it over, I was making a statement, a bit arrested, as to the revolution that has taken place in the girl, previous, well previous, to the scene of the great crisis, as to the attitude toward her of her sister's fiancé, from the moment she feels, exquisitely and almost incredulously feels, that difference in *him* (toward her) which has been more completely defined since her sister›s dismissal of him, and which gives her, as well as it gives him, a liberty never yet enjoyed by her. I shall presently come back to the rest of this, the enormous value to be got out of it; but I want not simply to brush by the small hare started yesterday by that sudden remembrance of the question of the portrait, the portrait figuring, or having figured, so extraordinarily to Ralph upwards of a century after its being painted; and which it would seem I must do something about. I see a chance to play with it, with the 1820 production of it, for illustration and intensification of my most-sought effect. It's an excrescence perhaps upon the surface I have already in this rough fashion plotted out; which remark, however, is nonsense, as nothing is an excrescence that I may interestingly, that I may contributively, work in. It gives me moreover, the idea I begin to clutch the tip of the tail of, it gives me another person whom I suddenly see as a great enhancement for my action; the painter-man who gets, doesn't one fancy? into a much straighter and closer "psychologic" and perceptive and mystified and mixed relation with his remarkable subject than any of the others in *their* way do. I get the painter-man as affected in his way too with the famous malaise, and the more affected with his proportionately greater opportunities, as it were, if not of observation at least of a kind of wondering and penetrating consideration. It "kind of" glimmers upon me that there would be something good, something much to the purpose, in having the painter-man *begin* to prepare the turn the situation takes, having him start the question of *what the matter is* (crudely speaking) with the genial young man, after all, and below and outside of his geniality; so that his wonderment, his felt queerness and queernesses, are inevitably communicated by him and sow the seed of the rest of what I want. They sow above all, don't they, or mayn't they be made to? the seed of Ralph's *suspicion of his being suspected*, putting him on his guard against this latter, rendering him uneasy, and whatever else, under the painter's study of him. Wouldn't it be then to the little H.W. man that the artist speaks of his strange impression, in complete confidence and secrecy at first, but sowing what I have called the seed so in the most favourable ground? I recognise that one doesn't quite see how we *know* he does this, as we don›t of course see or hear him do it; yet that needn›t find itself so ill provided for by Ralph's himself making it out and concluding upon it—which is after all the only way we really know anything. I don't want to repeat what I have done at least a couple of times, I seem to remember, and notably in The Liar—the "discovery", or the tell-tale representation of an element in the sitter written clear by the artist's projection of it on canvas. At the same time I am not afraid; I see its office well enough and needn't trouble if once the idea appeals, as I think it really does. In this case it's worked in early; the notion of my young man having his portrait as a matter of course done in London coming in with perfect naturalness. He has it done for his prospective bride; she takes an interest in it of the very greatest at first; and it is the little H.W. man who recommends, who selects, the artist. I see all sorts of curious things in this—it perfectly bristles with them, and with one's chance, above all, of making the personage in question (and I do want another figure, to people the canvas a little more) a real vision to Ralph, a character of the time, intensely typical for Ralph; through whose sense of all which, however, I tread the delicate ground of imputations to him, of perceptions, discriminations, estimates more or less at variance with his 1820 identity. That delicate ground, I have only to remind myself, is absolutely the very most attaching ground of my process; solvitur ambulando—I have only to find myself in close quarters with it to get from it force and felicity. I present then the painter-man, I make him, do him, see him and use him; use him to very good purpose. Don't I kind of see Ralph's suspicion of being suspected come to a head in the sight of something produced on the little H.W. man's part, on his nerves and in his fancy, in fine, through an active correspondence with the malaise the artist has caused in him through divinably feeling it himself? The foregoing difficult to state, but one is quite possessed of it; there's a great lot in it—only too much, alas, given my faculty for amplifying and going far. However, a rigorous tight hand on the excess of that is my very law of life here. I do feel how an effective further twist or two hangs about the question of the portrait. We get it surely as painted full face on—with the rendered face, in other words, that is turned away from Ralph's 1910 vision of him on that night in the house. Yes, he sits for it in 1820; he sees it grow, he sees and feels what grows out of it—I really don't see why the fact of it, the high conceit of it, mayn't do for me a good deal of my work. It plays a part in the situation—though I must square the difficulty of the artist "feeling about his sitter" as he more and more does and yet being able to keep his method and process, his application of his ability, well in hand, in order to put the thing through. It's a fine thing, a very fine one—I need it as that; for the finer it is the more it plays its part in the state of sensibility, all round, at which we increasingly assist. The thing is done for the prospective bride—though she would have been much more likely to have been treated to a fine miniature (alas, but no matter!) And don't I see that the first stroke in the reaction, on her part, as I may conveniently call it, is her abrupt, her sudden inconsequent refusal of the gift? in which she is backed by her mother. Perhaps she refuses it even before it is quite finished—for I want the artist to have spoken about it to the little H.W. man, so to put it, while the work is still in progress; which is also the time of the latter's opening himself about it (as Ralph "makes out") to the two women. Here I have something—the picture's having been destined for the big panel over the principal drawing-room—whereas the place in which my hero finds it in 1910 is the small inner retreat which I have handled in Book II. The mother and daughter startle Ralph, in 1820, by their expression of unwillingness to its hanging where it was intended; but as I want it still on the premises, want some compromise or right thing done about it, so that it shall be there for 1910, I see as arrangeable the business, the tension, the whole significant passage, of its being relegated to the place where everyone concerned will least see it—short of its being turned out of the house; a circumstance I *don't* invoke. I have it there for the other man, as his own portrait, when he is restored to his time by Ralph›s liberation from it; I have it there because I want him *in* it, don›t you see? for that wonder over it in which Ralph is held during his night of 1910. The other man comes back, the other man is *in* it, in order to carry out his part—well, of what I have recorded.

The "sacrifice", the indispensable, unspeakable sacrifice, on the girl's part, is involved in her relation to Ralph as she now knows him, and the quintessential "drama" of it, so to speak, is by the same token involved in *his knowing her* as she knows him, and as, above all, she is known *by* him. There hovers before me a something-or-other in this, a finer twist still, a deeper depth or higher flight of the situation, which seems worth looking into, and which in fact already appears to open out a good bit before me as I consider it. Isn't there something, isn't there even much, in the idea that when once these two have arrived, so to speak, at their understanding, at their mutual disclosures, or at least, that is, at his disclosure and her avowal, he becomes capable of a sort of sublimity in presence, as who should say, of her own? so that there is a kind of struggle between them as to who shall give up most—if I may put it in such a way without excess of the kind of romanticism that I don't want; wanting as I do above all, constantly kept hold of and economised, never let go of nor perverted in the least, the unfailing presence, drawing in everything to itself, of that force of "tone" which makes the thing of the parenté of the "Screw". So much is true and absolute; but doesn't prevent that I am wanting to put my finger on the very centre of the point from which my young man's "liberation" is worked. What hovers before me at this pitch, as I just said, is the *concetto* that, sincerely affected by her sublimity, he is moved to match it—and in all sincerity as I say—by offering to remain with her, as who should say, give up everything *for* her—from the moment he thus takes in that she gives him up for what is to herself utterly nothing, nothing but the exaltation of sacrifice—in short what I see! I have it all, I possess it here, and now must give pause to this long outciphering. It seems to give me after all a fourth recurrence of the man of 1820, called back, as it were, by what takes place. I possess it, I hold it fast; simply noting the prime point in regard to my last Book. Rather good and fine, I think, to make it that as the man of 1820 is "called" (since I think I do definitely give him his re-intervention here, though probably at the cost of still keeping these down to three in number, and so running two of the others, as who should say, into one,) so the woman of 1910 is likewise called; so my fundamental idea that the solution of the solution comes about through Aurora's "coming out, coming over", takes effect as I had planned it. The penultimate book ends on the climax I have in mind, as the "Ambassador" Book ended and broke off with the two at the door of the House; and so the ultimate one puts Ralph, always in London, and after the lapse of the real six months or whatever, face to face with his friend of Book I, to whom exactly what was foreshadowed in that Book for my dénoûment had happened. Things, things for her consciousness, her imagination, her growing unrest, her own New York malaise, have happened to *her* too; just how we are to know about them giving me, however, a little knot rightly to untie. I hate its being a "little" knot, savouring so of the perfunctory and the abbreviated; yet how can I want it in the nature of things to do more than adequately balance with the dimensions, or whatever, of Book First? The question is how, with the right sort of beauty of effect, to work in together the Ambassador's re-participation *and* her own, or rather, better put, hers and the Ambassador›s own; since I of course, under penalty of the last infamy, stick here still, as everywhere, to our knowing these things but through Ralph's knowing them. It's a bit awkward that I seem to want Aurora's arrival in London and her appeal to the Ambassador for assuagement of her literal climax of trouble, I seem to want that passage to precede my young man's reappearance, re-emergence, so to speak—and yet can't possibly have anything so artistically base. I want the "rescue", on this side of time, by Aurora, as the liberation, *for* rescue on the other side of time, has been by the girl of 1820; I want it to be, on our actual ground, by something that Aurora *does*; I want his restoration and recovery to take place actually and literally through her having got into such a "psychic" state, passed through such a psychic evolution, over there, that she takes action at last, takes the very action that she sort of defied Ralph to make her take in that full, and would-be at least so rich, "scene" of the most preliminary order. What there took place essentially was, as he formulated it, that she would look at none but a man of, as it were, tremendous action and adventure, not being appealed to (however she might attenuate or sophisticate her arrangement of her case) by the "mere" person, the mere leader, of the intellectual life, the mere liver in a cultivated corner, that Ralph has admitted himself to be to her—with a frankness, an abjection, say, that his whole subsequent adventure represents his reaction against. The immense scope his reaction has found then, once he has got over into the "old world", this has developed to the point that no prodigious adventure of any such figure as she may have had in mind comes within millions of miles of the prodigy of his adventure; whereby my conceit is that all the while he is "having" this, all the while she, left to the aftersense of what has passed between them, gradually feels her "state of mind", state of feeling, state of fancy, say, state of nerves in fine, grow and grow (in a sort of way that is corresponding all the while to the stages of his experience) till the pitch of unsupportable anxiety and wonder is reached for her, and being able no longer to stand it, she comes out to London. I make her come to London through considerations, references or whatever, plausible enough; and I make her by the same token want to see the Ambassador—whom she approaches, after the very fashion of Ralph's approach six months or whenever, before, and as if he were almost, so to say, a father-confessor. All this is feasible and "amusing", rather beautiful to do being what I mean; only it must come *after* and by reference backward, so to call it—as I can only make the Ambassador precede her in these renewals, for Ralph, of contact and apprehension. It isn›t so much making him aware of the Ambassador first, so to speak, that is the trouble, and making him then aware of Aurora *by* that personage and what comes of reference on his part to the beautiful uneasy and inquiring creature of New York; it isn›t so much the scene with that young woman herself then taking place: it isn't these that put their question to me, but the terms and conditions on and in which I have his Excellency and his young friend of the previous season confronted. What a blessing thus to find, accordingly, how the old gentle firmness of pressure, piously applied, doesn't fail to supply me. Our young friend is in the house again as he was in it in Book II—the only little hitch being that I didn't show him as *living* there, for the Ambassador, in Book III. He goes to live there, goes *with* that escort to do so on the last page of the Book, but by that very fact to pass into—well everything that we have seen him in and which represents the rupture of continuity with the Ambassador›s period. So in short, perfectly, I see that, for consummate reasons, he can't receive this visitor on that exhausted scene at all, but must have the case otherwise—have it in fact just as it comes to me now. The Ambassador, after his visit from Aurora (which we don't know about yet, don't know about till Ralph has *his* knowledge of it from him,) goes then, walks then, the day and the season being fine and he walking with the largeness with which dear J. R. L. used to walk—he goes then, I say, to the place where he has last had sight of his so interestingly demented young man of said previous season: he goes there but to have the sensation, by which I mean of course the actual experience, of seeing the very conditions in which he then parted with him practically renewed. The last thing he had stood there on the pavement before the house to see was Ralph's going in with that last look at him and with the open door duly again closing on him. So accordingly the first thing he now sees is Ralph's coming out again with the door closing on him from behind and the *first* look the young man addresses to the world of 1910 resting exactly upon the confidant of his former embroilment. I like that—like Ralph›s coming straight out of everything we have been having, everything up to the very last sharp edge of it, straight back into this friend's hands. Well, how do I take up, that is how does Ralph take up, and how does the Ambassador, this fresh situation and relation? The Ambassador, after his passage with the so handsome and so distracted young woman from New York, may well have some doubt and some question as to how, and be in some predicament about it; but I grant at once that Ralph has emerged from all trouble and now is, for the whole situation, supreme master and controller. *He* is «all right» at least, and he *re-connects*, on the spot, with all the lucidity and authority we can desire of him. His distinguished friend has come, clearly, on a visit to him—and he embraces that as well as he embraces their not going back into the house. At the previous season, as I have called it, he wasn't yet living in the house, he was only visiting it from his hotel or his lodgings; yet it isn't to these, none the less, that I see him invite his caller to adjourn with him, but, under the happiest inspiration, straight into the Square itself, very pleasant now to sit in (I must rightly and neatly adjust together the times of the year) and in which, under its ancient form, by which I mean of course its earlier, he has been through the scène à faire of 1820. It strikes me as positively "pretty" that they go into the Square together on the leafy June afternoon and that there it is, while they sit down, that the Ambassador reports to him of the visit received at the Embassy from Aurora. He has those things to *tell*—to tell to the young man who had those others to do the like with as presented in Book III; whereby it is very much he, or entirely he, who is the relator, reporter, exhibitor, with Ralph also for cross-questioner, as the Ambassador himself was on the other occasion—I myself having of course too my free hand for showing the elder man as really confessing to his genial bewilderment of interest. However, the extent to which I am possessed of this requires no dotting of "i's"; and the great point simply is that thus we get all we require, as a preliminary to the last pages of all of what has happened to or in, what has happened for and by, Aurora. I scarcely need state that the upshot or conclusion of the two men's talk is that Ralph must of course at once see that young woman; which is the understanding on which the Ambassador leaves him. But I am almost capable of wondering whether I had best give this meeting, this reunion of theirs, in the facts and in the flesh, as it were—so aloof do I feel from the possibility of a kind of graceless literality. I shall see, I shall make up my mind: it will come, in true rightness, it *can* come but so, when I get in close nearness to it. I do seem to conceive that I can beautifully get all my needed value for final climax from taking it all out, or putting it all in, between the two men—especially after they have come out of the Square together for the Ambassador to go, and they stand on the opposite pavement, the bit round the Square, with the house over there in view. Ralph of course has *told* his Excellency nothing; not a syllable of repetition of all that we›ve been having, of course, issues from him for his friend›s illumination. He has only cross-questioned, only extracted everything about Aurora; only taken in *how* his triumph is complete and how that young woman has come down and round. It is thus a question then of his sending her a message, and of his sending it by the Ambassador for whom he sees her (justified thereto very vividly by the latter) simply and all so wonderingly wait. Yes, the message he sends is that he shall be glad to see her. He summons her to him—doesn't offer to go to her. He has said to his companion at first and for their going into the Square that he is not staying at the House, and that his lodgings are elsewhere. The Ambassador, taking the message, has the question, virtually: "She's to come then to you at your hotel?" On which, after an hesitation and resting his eyes a moment over on the house, Ralph says: "No, no. Over there." But I should say I needn't here and now draw this out, and that I have it all and more than all, were it not that I just want to note more emphatically that I provide for everything, provide against the need of any "small" scene with the young woman from New York as a sequence to this full passage with the Ambassador, and as a wind up to the whole thing, together with the balance of such a chapter against the preliminary Book First—I provide for everything, I say, by putting *into* this *finale* between the two men in the Square, by making Ralph acquaint his visitor with, so to speak, *all* the requisite meaning resident in the appeal, from their young woman, that his Excellency has called to report on. I said above that Ralph «tells» the Ambassador nothing—but only receives his own statement and cross-questions him on it; but that qualification refers only to what has been happening to R., in his prodigious alternate character, during the previous six months or whatever. Not a word about all that; but on the other hand every word required to enable us to dispense with another scene for the young woman from N.Y. On that subject Ralph is fully informing, and what I mean and want is that this action in him, holding his interlocutor extraordinarily interested, shall so suffice for our own interest and satisfaction, shall so vividly take the place of it, that we simply shan't in the least miss, but shall find ourselves admirably do without, any bringing "on" again of Aurora. The present and conclusive scene in the Square all sufficiently brings her on, all sufficiently prefigures Ralph's reunion, not to say union, with her, and in short acquits me of everything. A far more ingenious stroke, surely, and to be made more ministrant to effect and to the kind of note of the strange that I want than the comparatively platitudinous direct *duo* between the parties! He has only to give us in advance all that the duo must and will consist of in order to leave us just where, or at least just *as*, we want!

[1] The original version of *The Sense of the Past*, revised by the author in 1914 (see Preface,) broke off in the middle of the scene between Ralph Pendrel and the Ambassador (Book III). Having reached this point in the revision Henry James dictated the following notes before proceeding further.